THE ALKALINE COOKBOOK

THE
ALKALINE
COOKBOOK

DR. STEPHAN DOMENIG

FX MAYR HEALTH CENTER *The Original*

modern books

PRAISE FOR THE ALKALINE CURE BOOK

'There's no need to jet off to Austria to reap the benefits of The Original FX Mayr Health Centre, a favourite cleansing retreat of Uma Thurman and Gwyneth Paltrow. With The Alkaline Cure you can lose weight, gain energy, boost your metabolism and feel young – all from the comfort of your own home.' – Alexia Dellner, *Women's Health* magazine

'It shows you how to prepare yourself and your shelves for the best possible plan results, and promises to leave you lighter, brighter and with bucketloads more energy in just a matter of days…The Alkaline Cure is fast becoming our healthy holiday must-have.' – Emma Jones, *Get the Gloss*

'Not only does it give me ideas for healthy recipes but more importantly, it gives me a philosophy with which to live by … it is not a fad or an extreme diet. It is a book written on well founded principles by a medical practitioner with lots of experience'.
– Susan Thira, the *Happy Healthy Mumma* blog

'Alongside fantastic recipes, the book clearly explains the principles of the alkaline cure and preparing to go alkaline. Besides weight loss, the approach will also give clearer skin, reduced signs of ageing and much more.'
– *Yoga Magazine*

'As acid is reduced, chronic cellular inflammation begins to subside…sure, there are other anti-inflammatory diets out there – but most eliminate both dairy and starch. The Alkaline Cure gets the same results without the deprivation.' – *Woman's World* magazine

PRAISE FOR THE ALKALINE APPROACH

'This is about much more than a good rest; it is about regaining your health ... it is simply learning to eat properly. I feel calm and rested, balanced and healthy.' – Alice Thomas, *Mail Online*

'The single most effective change you can make to your health is to increase your intake of alkaline-forming foods. Ideally, two thirds of every meal you eat should be alkaline and only one third acid.'
– *The Mail on Sunday,* You Magazine

'I came back feeling happier, calmer and looking brighter – lighter too, I have lost 6 lbs ...' – Gwyneth Paltrow, *Elle* magazine

'It's the slow-burning trend that's taking the celebrity diet world by storm. The alkaline diet is great for your digestive system, can give you clearer skin, increased energy, stronger immunity and better sleep ...'
– Jess Commons, *Grazia* magazine

'A proven wellbeing programme that can change lives ... the Mayr approach to wellbeing centres around one word – balance.'
– Hilary Boddie, *European Spa* magazine

'Four months on and my stomach still hasn't bloated (not even after meals), my eyes are brighter, I feel energised, rested and have been happier at work.'
– *Psychologies* magazine

'A healthier, long-term approach to eating and living.'
– Pamela Goodman, *House and Garden* magazine

CONTENTS

INTRODUCTION

Dr Stephan Domenig,
Medical Director

Over one hundred years ago, Dr Franz Xaver Mayr recognised the importance of a healthy digestive system on the overall health of the body. He realised that eating too much, too quickly, and the wrong foods causes indigestion and acidity – and that setting this right could bring a whole host of benefits. Increased energy, weight loss, refreshed skin and hair, a strong immune system and healthy brain function are just some of these.

The Mayr philosophy does not treat illness but, rather, focuses on good health, and the way to achieve that is to look after the biggest organ in the body – the stomach itself. If the stomach functions properly then so will everything else. If a part of the stomach is impaired in some way, then the whole of the rest of the system suffers. Food is your best medicine and a balance of the right foods at the right time of day is your own therapy.

I came to the original FX Mayr clinic to help people rediscover their natural health through eating and living well. My first book, *The Alkaline Cure*, has encouraged people to do this in their own homes. Now, through this collection of recipes, it will be even easier to build a lifestyle that can stand you in good stead throughout your whole life.

Our recipes and way of cooking have evolved and developed over many decades and every year we add more recipes that are tested both medically by our doctors and by our guests. Those in this book have been adapted for the home cook, but the principles are the same. This is food that will be good for you, and that tastes good.

This is not necessarily a vegetarian philosophy. Instead, the focus is on restoring balance to an acidic body by increasing your intake of alkaline foods and rediscovering a life that is at one with your natural rhythms. The recipes nurture your stomach by providing it with the full spectrum of foods that it requires, as we know that the stomach and digestive system are vital in keeping your whole body healthy.

Cooking should be enjoyable both in the making and the eating! We should take advantage of the fresh, seasonal fruits and vegetables that are available at different times of the year to create dishes that are nourishing and delicious, but that also pay attention to the natural rhythms of the body. We use practical ingredients that are easy to find and affordable – you don't need to splash out on nutria-exotica such as amaranth or chia seeds to balance your body and feel better.

Some fundamental principles and types of cooking will be invaluable if you are to take the first steps towards an alkaline lifestyle. In the first part of the book, we will guide you through the initial steps, explaining the philosophy behind an alkaline way of life. Making soups, baking easy homemade breads and crackers, and understanding the secrets of delicious salads are also covered here. The recipes are then arranged seasonally, with options for every time of day and occasion, as well as five easy ideas to make use of eight of the best and most accessible alkaline vegetables.

The key to better health and an improved quality of life is right in front of you. Take the first steps and find out how good you can really feel, naturally.

FX MAYR HEALTH CENTER *The Original*

❇

1
Why Alkaline?

EAT WELL, LIVE WELL, AGE WELL

'I noticed changes in just two weeks…I had more vitality, my skin wasn't dry, I stopped craving sugar, my mood stabilised, everything became more balanced.'

– Elle Macpherson, *Body + Soul*

Your nutrition affects everything about you – how fast you age, your weight, the quality of your skin, organs, your energy levels and productivity, your mood and emotions and your immune system. It has a powerful impact on your quality of life. While it's important to cure or treat our current ailments and diseases through good diet, the key word is prevention – through good nutrition we can prevent ourselves becoming ill in the first place. We can prevent the damage to our bodies and to our lives by building an alkaline way of life.

The cure provides a simple set of diet and lifestyle principles that work holistically to improve your overall health and wellbeing. Through a rebalancing of your digestive system and an increase in alkaline food intake, your metabolism will function properly and your body will return to its naturally healthy state. Put simply, eating alkaline is the best diet choice you can make to stay healthy as you age.

The Alkaline Cookbook provides you with easy-to-follow and delicious recipes that will enable you to make good diet choices, decrease your acidity and enjoy delicious meals all year round. You won't have to give up the things you love; you will simply look at revising the balance. Our ideal ratio for each plate is 4:1 alkaline/acid or a minimum of 2:1; if you have overindulged for a few days then simply be mindful of this and increase your intake of alkaline foods over the following few days. Our motto is: Eat well, live well, age well.

Signs of an Acid Body

Some of the most common symptoms of acid overload may well be familiar to you.

- » Dry, brittle hair and nails
- » Dry, prematurely wrinkled, itchy and sagging skin
- » Cellulite
- » Eczema
- » Cancer, diabetes, heart disease
- » Brittle bones and osteoporosis
- » Muscle and joint pain
- » Infertility
- » Constipation
- » Obesity
- » Bloating
- » Heartburn
- » Bad breath
- » Gum disease
- » Cracked, discoloured teeth
- » Inflamed, sensitive gums
- » Bloodshot, itchy, watery eyes
- » Depression
- » Irritability
- » Insomnia and fatigue
- » Lack of energy and focus
- » Headaches
- » Frequent colds and flu
- » Cravings for sugar and salt
- » Tendency to feel cold

WHY WE ALL NEED TO EAT ALKALINE

Our damaging acidic way of life is so ingrained in society that we fail to recognise an acute and very real danger – that our lifestyle is killing us. Here's how:

Too Much Food

Many of us have become so used to huge portions and an endless supply of food that we overeat on a daily basis. Overloading your digestive system means that it is unable to process what you eat properly, leading to increased acid and a range of digestive problems.

The Wrong Food

Likewise, processed convenience foods have shifted the balance from local, seasonal produce to ready-made, pre-packaged foods with added salt, sugar and fats and limited nutritional value. In addition, unless we are serious athletes, we eat too much animal protein – which is one of the most acidic foods. Protein diets may cause weight-loss in the short term but they will destroy the body's healthy acid/alkaline balance.

Eating too Fast and too Late

We are all guilty of rushing our meals, eating on the run, eating without thinking. Eating too fast also results in eating too much as the brain does not have time to register that the stomach is full. Equally, eating a heavy meal late in the evening only puts more pressure on the digestive system at a time when it should be resting.

Stress

Our bodies are designed to cope with stress to a certain extent. However, long-term chronic stress not only damages the stress-managing adrenal gland and the thyroid, but also forms acid in the body. The stomach, in particular, reacts badly to stress – it stops functioning, meaning that nutrients are not efficiently absorbed.

Sedentary Lifestyle

The human body is designed to be energetic, with strong skin and bones and an efficient metabolism. Yet increasingly we are becoming more inactive, especially as we age. We drive too much and we sit down for long periods of time, when naturally we should be walking and moving our bodies.

ALKALINE PRINCIPLES FOR HEALTHY LIVING

These are the simple principles that guide an alkaline diet and way of life – following them will help you to lead an effortlessly alkaline life.

Eat Mindfully

It is important to be aware of what you are eating and how you are eating it. Take your time and chew at least thirty times to break down solids into manageable portions, otherwise you are asking your stomach to do the work for you. Your stomach is not designed to break down large pieces of food, so they pass through without delivering their quota of nutrients and vitamins. Give yourself at least thirty minutes to eat.

Eat the Right Quantities of the Right Foods

Local, seasonal foods will be richer in nutrients, fresher, naturally ripe and less likely to have been processed, meaning that you will get the most from each vegetable, fruit and grain. However, it is not a question of only eating alkaline foods. The optimal alkaline-acid balance to aim for at each meal is four parts alkaline to one part acid; or at least aim for a 2:1 ratio.

Breakfast like a King, Dine like a Pauper

In the morning our bodies are fresh and rested and we have the entire day to absorb and process what we eat, so our earlier meals should be the most substantial. Eat your main meal at lunch, and a light dish such as soup for an early dinner, to allow for the slowing down of the digestive system

Drink, Drink, Drink…

Most of us do not drink enough. We need about two litres of liquid a day to be properly hydrated – be that water or herb and vegetable tea. Drink before or after meals, but not during, as this washes down food without it being properly chewed. The saliva in our mouths created by chewing is the first part of the digestive process and is very important.

Raw Only before Four

Avoid raw foods in the evening when your digestive system should be calming down.

Exercise Regularly and Moderately

A healthy digestive system needs a healthy body that is not overweight. Be gentle with yourself, but make sure that you spend thirty minutes each day stretching your body and letting your heart pump new oxygenated blood to all your vital organs. Get into a routine that you enjoy, and your body will thank you.

Cleanse and Rest

It is important to let your stomach and mind recuperate. Give yourself periods of time in which you consume only teas and water before reintroducing simple foods. You can also mix a small amount of baking soda with water to stimulate the digestive system and alkalise the stomach. Make sure you get fresh air, switch off electronic devices and bring plants or flowers into the home.

Find your Own Rhythm

It would be naïve to think we could give up our stressful jobs, but it is important to find your own personal way of living a gentler life. Try to switch off when the day is over and take moments to reflect during busy periods. Create breaks throughout the day to eat and set up helpful routines such as a mid-morning walk or stretching exercises.

BENEFITS OF ALKALINE LIVING

While the greatest benefits of an alkaline lifestyle will be life-long, some will become apparent in weeks, and even days.

Slows Down the Signs of Ageing
While nothing can stop the onset of ageing, following alkaline principles will help you to look and feel healthy and youthful. Better mineralisation in the body improves nails, hair and skin.

Renews Energy and Vitality
When your body is expending large amounts of energy in processing food but not receiving the nutrients it needs as repayment, you will become tired and lacklustre. Addressing this, encouraging oxygen into the body and regulating eating and sleeping patterns, will inevitably increase your energy.

Encourages Peaceful, Deep Sleep
You will find that sleep comes easily when your body is working to the rhythms of your day. Better digestion, regular bowel movements, physical relaxation, emotional harmony, increased blood circulation and an avoidance of stimulants also aid a restful sleep.

Encourages Weight Loss
An alkaline diet will help you to find your natural body weight. If overweight, this will result in slimming.

Reduces Bloating and Constipation
An alkaline diet will encourage regular and healthy bowel movements and bladder function, removing unnecessary stresses on your system.

Defends against Allergy and Disease
A healthy digestive system supports a healthy immune system, helping to protect against the development of disease and of food allergies.

Improves Mood and Brain Function

Acid imbalance is clinically proven as a major factor in psychological and stress-related ailments. The vitamins and amino acids provided by an alkaline diet – along with a focus on mindful living – not only help to alleviate stresses, but also increase the effective performance of the brain.

Strengthens Bones

Alkaline minerals, calcium and vitamin D support healthy bones and alleviate aches and pains. Eating foods rich in these vitamins and minerals also means that the body is not forced to use calcium from bones to counterbalance acids in the system.

Increases Fertility

An alkaline diet restores a balanced milieu in the gut, improving absorption of food and guaranteeing the proper activation of bacteria to support digestion. Perfect absorption equals perfect nourishment of cells, including those for reproduction.

THE BEAUTY OF BALANCE

At the clinic, we know that the first step in addressing an acid imbalance is to educate people about what foods they should be eating, and which they should avoid.

All the foods we eat can be classified as either acid-forming or alkaline-forming, meaning the foods release an acid or alkaline residue during the process of digestion. Note that foods that have an acidic taste (such as lemons) are not necessarily acid-forming. In this book, when we describe foods as 'acid' or 'alkaline', we mean acid-forming or alkaline-forming.

Although we emphasise strongly the important role of vegetables, the alkaline diet is neither vegan nor vegetarian. Some foods, including meat, are defined as acid-forming but still have a valuable role to play in the diet, bringing vitamins and other minerals. What we want is the right acid/alkaline balance. The majority of the recipes in this book focus on natural, plant-based foods, with the protein element as a nutritional – and gastronomic – enhancement. Depending on where you live, the foods available will be different, but it is important that we do not lose that rich mix of fresh and varied ingredients in any one meal. Eating a wide variety of foods, focusing on balance and mindful eating, and listening to the natural rhythms of your digestive system will lead to a body that is in tune with itself.

Managing Cravings

When you start out, you may well feel withdrawal symptoms from the acid ingredients that your body craves. This is because your body is addicted to them – but a craving suggests an imbalance and deficiency in vital vitamins and nutrients. You will soon find yourself craving the foods your body really needs, and enjoying natural flavours without the addition of salt and sugar.

Portion Control

The digestive system can only cope with so much food, and needs time to process it – generally around four hours. If you overeat, and most of us do, you overload your stomach, slowing down the digestive process and preventing it from absorbing all the vitamins and minerals that it needs. One of the easiest ways to ensure a smaller portion is to use a smaller plate or bowl. Instead of a large amount of meat and two vegetables, think about a smaller piece of meat and four vegetables. Keep in mind that you really don't need the amount of protein that you think you do: not more than seventy grams at any meal. Also, be sure to eat slowly and mindfully rather than in a rush. All of these will help you eat less.

Plan Your Meals

Take time to think about what you will want to eat for the week and buy ahead. Making a batch of breakfast spread and a soup that can last all week will mean that you are prepared if you have to travel. Likewise, have some homemade dips, crispbreads, nuts and fresh vegetables on hand throughout the day to give you energy and keep your metabolism moving. Think about what you will eat and how it will add up over the day and weeks – instead of calorie counting, be aware of the value of each food you eat and the role it plays in your continued good digestion.

ACID FOOD GROUPS

While our main aim is for a balanced diet, there are some foods that are inherently acid-forming.

Meat: How Much is too Much?

We have become accustomed to eating meat every day, excluding other foods and creating an imbalance, but we can find protein and amino acids in other ways too – through grains and alternatives such as tofu. Eat gentler meats such as fish and game in small quantities.

Sugars

There is enough natural sugar in our diet without supplementing it. Unfortunately, we have been tricked into depending on highly acidic artificial sweeteners and refined sugar, craving these when, in fact, they are scientifically unnecessary. Sugar tricks the digestive system, inhibiting proteins and starches as they pass through the body. For more information on sugars, see page 49.

Alcohol and Caffeine

Alcohol and caffeine deplete vital minerals in the body. Alcohol also disrupts blood-sugar levels, stimulates cravings and lessens nutrient absorption. This being said, we do not expect you to abstain for the rest of your life – an occasional glass can be enjoyed.

Refined and Processed Foods

These foods are often high in sugar and salt, with most of their natural vitamins and minerals depleted due to over-processing. They can also contain artificial ingredients that the body is not designed to deal with, so vital organs are strained as the digestive system fights to break them down. Processed products provide bulk rather than nutrition.

Dairy

Most cow's dairy products are acid as they are essentially made up of fat and protein, and pasteurisation further depletes their nutritional value. However, dairy can be part of an alkaline lifestyle if small quantities of the right products are consumed.

ALKALINE FOOD GROUPS

Alkaline-forming foods should make up the majority of your intake.

Vegetables
Fresh, local vegetables are a vital part of alkaline living, providing important vitamins and minerals and the base for almost every meal.

Healthy Fats
Unsaturated fats provide energy and ensure healthy skin, brain and nerve function. High-quality, cold-pressed 'virgin' oils are best, but should be added at the end of cooking to preserve their nutrients. You'll also find these fats in nuts and seeds.

Whole Grains
Grains are nutritious and a valuable source of energy-giving complex carbohydrates. Commercial wheat, however, is often highly processed and contains high amounts of irritative gluten. Other grain crops such as rye, quinoa and buckwheat provide healthier fibre alternatives.

Ripe Fruits
As fruit ripens naturally, its nutritional content increases. Locally grown fruit is best, but exotic fruits are also great sources. Dried fruits are a helpful source of fibre, but check that they are naturally dried, without sugar or preservatives. Remember to take your time and chew well – food that ferments due to insufficient digestion forms acids.

Fresh Dairy
Fresh, young and organic products made from sheep's or goat's milk are best as our bodies are more familiar with the products of these animals, and they are generally produced in smaller quantities. See page 48 for more information on lactose and dairy.

Fresh Herbs and Spices
These are fundamentally alkaline ingredients, rich in vitamins and minerals. Start thinking about herbs and spices as ingredients in themselves, rather than just final additions.

CHOOSING ALKALINE

Be aware of what is in your shopping basket by following these rules for which foods to enjoy ▲ and which to reduce ▽.

DAIRY AND ALTERNATIVES

▽ Mature cow's milk cheeses and cream cheese.

▲ Butter, fresh milk, probiotics such as live yoghurt, coconut milk, almond milk, fresh/young cheeses, curd cheese, cream and crème fraîche, goat's milk and goat's cheese.

GRAINS AND CEREALS

▽ All refined grains and refined white-flour products, egg noodles, white rice, pasta, wholemeal bread, wholemeal pasta and cornflour.

▲ Almond flour, amaranth, oatmeal, quinoa, wild rice, buckwheat, millet, brown rice, semolina, spelt, farro, soba noodles, rye, crispbreads. Bulgur wheat, polenta, pearl barley and couscous should be limited but can be enjoyed.

FRUITS AND VEGETABLES

▲ Enjoy all water-based vegetables, roots, tubers, mushrooms, bulbs, leaves and greens as well as ripe fruits, both local and exotic. Fermented vegetables such as kimchi and sauerkraut, sea vegetables like wakame and kelp, and naturally dried fruits are alkaline too. Leguminous plants that provide protein, such as beans, can be enjoyed in smaller quantities.

FATS

▽ Refined oils, margarine and low-fat spreads.

▲ Cold-pressed, virgin oils such as olive, linseed and pumpkin — these should be used cold. Good fats also come from nuts and seeds.

PROTEIN

▽ Beef, pork, chicken, lamb, turkey, bacon, sausages, salamis and all factory-farmed and processed meats. Limit your shellfish intake.

▲ Fish, wild and game meats, eggs, non-animal sources such as legumes and tofu.

HERBS, SPICES AND CONDIMENTS

▽ Refined sugar (white and brown), corn syrup, jams, maple syrup, artificial sweeteners, chocolate, peanut butter, mustard, balsamic vinegar, shop-bought mayonnaise or sauces, yeast, table salt.

▲ All herbs and spices, sea salt, mineral rock salt, shoyu, tahini, tamari, miso, apple cider vinegar. Use honey, agave syrup or stevia if you need sweetener.

2
Getting Started

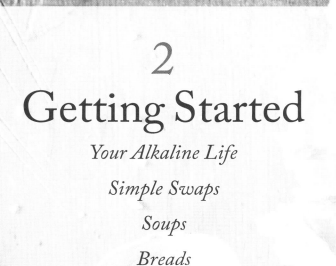

YOUR ALKALINE LIFE

Now that you have learnt about the main principles of an alkaline lifestyle and the amazing benefits it can bring, you should be ready to take the next step. Whatever your reasons for turning to an alkaline diet, there are some easy introductory measures that can help you along the way.

KEEP A FOOD DIARY

When making a dietary change, it is important to understand how your body – and your emotions – work. How have you reached the stage that you are currently at? What is your body trying to tell you?

A great way to find this out is to keep a food diary for one week. You will be surprised how quickly you notice the patterns and quick fixes that arise from mindless eating, and at the high volume of acidic, harmful foods and drinks that you put into your body on a daily basis.

An important part of keeping a food diary will also be acknowledging your triggers. All of us have certain times when we reach for a cup of coffee, a slice of cake or a plate of chips for comfort, but the truth is that while these foods might provide a quick lift, in the long run they will only add to stresses on the body and mind, and perpetuate the endless cycle of highs and lows. Take time to read through your food diary, see what sets you off, and prepare for it the next time. Trigger moments often include emotions such as boredom, tiredness, anxiety or low self-esteem, or stressful situations like being busy at work, skipping meals or having drunk alcohol. Most often, fear of breaking a habit can halt our progress, but planning ahead to avoid these situations will mean that you don't panic when they do arise.

SIMPLE SWAPS

The unhealthy behavioural patterns that we fall into are often down to continually choosing the wrong path, when there are easy alternatives ready to be taken. Below are some easy changes you can make to avoid a trigger moment resulting in an acid reaction.

▽ MILK CHOCOLATE

▲ **HIGH PERCENTAGE CACAO DARK CHOCOLATE**

Natural cacao is a fantastic source of antioxidants and magnesium, but commercial milk chocolate is pumped full of sugar and dairy fats. A square of good-quality dark chocolate is delicious, good for you and wards off unhelpful sweet cravings.

▽ TEA AND COFFEE

▲ **HERBAL AND VEGETABLE TEAS**

Natural stimulants such as ginger and peppermint will perk you up without the unnecessary acidity and inevitable crash.

▽ CHEDDAR, EMMENTAL AND PARMESAN

▲ **FRESH GOAT'S AND SHEEP'S MILK CHEESES**

Dairy provides natural minerals and beneficial probiotics for the gut. However, products made from cow's milk are harder to digest and often trigger intolerances, so replacing these with small amounts of sheep's or goat's milk cheese or other alternatives is an easy step to take towards alkaline living.

▽ SHOP-BOUGHT JUICES, SMOOTHIES AND SOUPS

▲ **HOMEMADE ALTERNATIVES**

All of these can be made in advance and bottled up to take with you. As well as being free from added sugar, they will contain the whole fruit or vegetable (so all the vitamins), and you can add your own extras, such as nuts, seeds and oils.

▽ REFINED WHEAT FLOUR BREADS

▲ **NATURAL ALTERNATIVES**

Rye bread in particular is easy to find in supermarkets and more satisfying and lower in sugar and salt than commercial yeast breads.

YOUR ALKALINE KITCHEN

The most important thing you will need when cooking is a BIG saucepan. Sit it on your hob and when you drain vegetables or grains, add the liquid in to make stock. If you want to take an alkaline diet seriously, then having both an alkaline minestrone and a vegetable tea to hand is going to take you a long way down the road, and this stock will be crucial for those. Likewise, a loaf of spelt bread and a spread are always handy to keep in the kitchen.

Nearly everything in this book is based around fresh foods and preparing them from scratch. Make space in your kitchen for the seasonal, organic and local vegetables that will form the basis of your diet. Try to buy loose vegetables, too, because packets tend to make you over-buy and are a false economy – buying just the fresh ingredients that you need, in smaller amounts, means that what you eat contains the maximum nutrition and will not cost the earth.

You will also need a big fruit bowl to remind you that you have fresh fruit available all the time. It is important to let fruit ripen – the easiest way to do that is to place the less ripe foods next to the riper ones (particularly bananas, which ripen quickly) to bring them on.

Lots of fresh herbs – either growing in pots, or bunches kept with the stems in a glass of water – will be invaluable, too.

Portions and Leftovers

Meal recipes in this book use the amount of ingredients needed for one person, but this is easily doubled or quadrupled as required. Occasionally, dishes made for sharing, such as our alkaline Sunday roast, will serve more. Soup recipes all make one litre, as these can be stored and reheated for dinners later on in the week, and spreads make enough to last too.

If you have vegetables left over from a recipe, store them for use in another recipe, add them to the stockpot, make them into a soup or simply snack on them raw. If you continue to cook with alkaline ingredients, a natural shopping rhythm will find its way into your life, with fresh fruit and vegetables bought and used up often, and key spices, herbs and dried ingredients always at hand.

STOCKING UP

If you are going to make a good start on your alkaline life, it makes all the difference to be prepared. Having a selection of basic alkaline ingredients to hand means that you won't need to reach for a quick fix when you're feeling hungry. Your alkaline kitchen should include the following:

The Fridge

>> Leftover spreads and soups
>> A little fresh fish or meat
>> Butter, fresh curd and fresh sheep's or goat's milk cheese
>> Probiotic yoghurt
>> Nut milks
>> Salad items

The Larder

>> Vegetables and fresh fruit
>> A good selection of dried herbs and spices
>> Healthy fats and oils such as virgin olive oil and coconut butter
>> Grains such as spelt or farro, couscous, amaranth, polenta, and quinoa
>> Natural sweeteners
>> Nuts and seeds and vacuum-packed chestnuts
>> Unsweetened dried fruits such as apricots, raisins and cherries
>> Good-quality dark chocolate
>> Dried seaweed such as wakame
>> Dried mushrooms

SOUPS

Homemade vegetable soup is a satisfying, rewarding and quick way to go alkaline. All those basic, cheap year-round staples – carrots, potato, celery, broccoli, leeks and onion – are alkaline and make great soups.

Soup-making can also be a calming, meditative pleasure. A good trick is to have soup in the evening for supper – it is easy to digest, reassuring and filling. Equally, if you have a busy schedule at work a carton or flask takes care of lunch.

A Few Myths about Making Soup

Many old-fashioned recipes suggest cooking down the onions and vegetables in butter or oil to create a base, but that is not really necessary – simmering works fine. Old books also tend to give instructions for lengthy cooking times, but this generally refers to meat-based stocks and soups. Overcooking vegetables will boil off essential vitamins and minerals – twenty to thirty minutes is fine.

What You Need

Root vegetables are nearly all alkaline – and store well. Kale, spinach, broccoli and cabbage bring big splashes of green. Herbs, too, are valuable – especially the stems of parsley and coriander. And, as a final flourish, add in garlic, ginger, pine nuts, horseradish or spices like nutmeg, all of which are alkaline. When you are ready to make your soup, bear in mind these two helpful tips:

» Let it steep. Once you have finished the cooking, the juices will carry on leaching into the liquid making it more flavoursome.

» If you are in a hurry, grate the vegetables into the pan so they cook more quickly. If not, try to cut your vegetables into neat, spoon-sized cubes before cooking.

THE BASICS OF MAKING SOUP

There are levels to making a great soup and you don't have to go all the way in one giant step.

First Day Soup

Fill a big pan with water and simmer chopped vegetables, with skins if possible, for thirty to forty minutes. Onions are essential, although in more delicate soups leeks or shallots can do the job. Herby celery, thickening potatoes and carrots, parsnips or sweet potatoes, which add sweetness, are all staples. Vegetables such as celeriac and fennel work well, but are strong alkalising flavours. Green vegetables can be added ten minutes before the end.

Second Day Soup

The next day, divide the soup in two. Bring one half of the soup back to the simmer, add half a good handful of fresh spinach, let it wilt, and blend. You could also use a packet of frozen peas, add a tablespoon of cream or yoghurt or add some chopped herbs or spices.

Third Day Soup

From here you can build up a showpiece alkaline minestrone by adding a little of the following:

» Grains for texture and fibre. Use one, for example farro, brown rice, bulgur wheat or pearl barley, and simmer on their own first so that they do not soak up all of your soup.

» Pulses are not strictly alkaline but provide protein and in the context of a busy soup like this, the percentages are small. Tinned are quicker and easier than dried, but they need to be rinsed in clean water first. The smaller pulses like lentils and adzuki can be cooked from dry and contrast with bigger beasts like chickpeas, cannellini and butter beans.

» By this point the soup will be quite substantial, but many of the great soups like Italian ribollita and minestrone go a step further with shredded bread and broken-up pasta. Use alkaline breads or wholewheat pasta.

EVERYDAY ALKALINE SOUP

Now you have learnt the basics, put them into action with this staple, fat-free soup. It can be enjoyed at every stage for a hearty alkaline supper. Add to it as you like, and make it last all week.

Everyday Alkaline Soup Day One
Add more or different vegetables according to the seasons, aiming for an equal ratio of each.

3 litres water	2 celery stalks
1 large or two medium onions	Bunch of parsley
1 leek	1 broccoli head
1 carrot	Half a cauliflower

Bring the water to a simmer in a large pan. Peel, quarter and slice the onion and add to the mix. Top, tail and cut the leek across into small rings. Slice the carrot and celery lengthways, then cut up into small dice. Cut the stalks off the parsley and add them, keeping the leaves back to garnish later. Simmer, covered, for ten minutes. Chop the stem off the broccoli and cut up into dice and add to the mix, holding the florets back. Cut the cauliflower into small sections and add to the mix. Add in the broccoli heads for the last five minutes. In total simmer for twenty-five minutes. Serve with freshly chopped parsley.

Topping it Off – Alkaline Pesto
A herb-based pesto, of garlic, pine nuts and basil or parsley with oil can add another layer of taste to the soup. Or, even simpler, drizzle a fruity olive oil or pumpkin oil into the bowl.

1 tablespoon pine nuts	2 tablespoons olive oil
2 garlic cloves	1 lemon
1 bunch basil	

In a pestle and mortar (or a blender), grind the pine nuts, garlic and basil. Loosen the mix with olive oil and a squeeze of lemon.

Everyday Alkaline Soup Day Two

This is an easy trick that brings with it all the nutritional iron of spinach. If you want to go a step further, you can also use peas. Cabbage or kale work too, but let them cook for five or six minutes before liquidising. Keep back half the base soup for tomorrow and top up with any vegetable water you have left over from your cooking as you go.

1 litre alkaline soup   2 tablespoons parsley
100 g frozen peas   1 tablespoon yoghurt
Good handful of   Nutmeg
   fresh spinach

Bring the soup back to a simmer. Add in the peas. As it boils, throw in the spinach leaves. Mix them in well and allow to darken – about one minute. Take off the heat. Add in the parsley. Blend. Serve with a tablespoon of yoghurt and a grating of nutmeg.

Everyday Alkaline Soup Day Three

Transform your soup into a busy alkaline-rich minestrone. You can go a stage further and add in chunks of stale bread or cooked pasta or even a tin of tomatoes, but this is pretty crowded already.

1 litre alkaline soup   100 g lentils
100 g farro   200 g tinned butter beans

Bring a clean pan of water to the boil and add the farro and the lentils to cook together for about twenty minutes, until soft. Drain and combine with the alkaline soup. Bring back to a simmer. Rinse the butter beans under running water, until the water runs clear. Add to the soup. Serve the soup with a tablespoon of olive oil or Alkaline Pesto (see page 36) drizzled on top.

BREADS

Some people like to bake, while others find it too much trouble. Some people like big processors in their kitchen to let bread knead automatically – others like to use their hands. Whichever you are, try these staple breads – it will be worth it to know what goes into your loaf. If yeast is an issue then making bread without it is straightforward and worth the effort, especially for the breakfast spreads in this book.

MAYR SPELT BREAD

This is the famous FX Mayr spelt bread, which was designed to encourage clients to re-learn the enjoyment of chewing. It was originally always served with fennel soup. You make your own starter without packaged yeast by preparing the sourdough the night before.

For the Sourdough Starter

125 g live yoghurt made from sheep's or goat's milk

125 ml water
125 g spelt flour

For the Bread

750 g spelt flour
250 ml warm water
1 tablespoon cream of tartar
½ teaspoon rock or sea salt

½ teaspoon coriander seed
½ teaspoon cumin
½ teaspoon fennel
Sourdough starter (as above)

Mix all the sourdough ingredients together in a bowl by hand. Leave to stand, covered, for eight hours in a warm place (approximately 28°C). Cover with a tea towel.

The next day, mix all the ingredients together with the sourdough. Using a processor, mix well for eight to ten minutes – or you can knead by hand on a floured surface. Bake for thirty minutes at around 180°C.

HOMEMADE PITTA BREAD WITH YEAST

250 g strong wholemeal flour,
 plus extra for dusting
7 g sachet instant yeast
1 teaspoon sea salt

160 ml water
2 teaspoons olive oil, plus
 extra for kneading

In a bowl, mix the flour, yeast and salt. Add 120 ml of the water and one and a half teaspoons of oil. Mix the ingredients together with your fingers. Gradually add the remaining water and oil until all the flour has come away from the sides of the bowl and you have a soft but not sticky dough. Pour a little oil onto your work top. Place the dough on top and knead for five to ten minutes. When it is smooth and no longer wet, place the dough in a clean, oiled bowl. Cover and leave to double in size.

   Preheat the oven to 250°C and place a baking tray or baking stone on the middle shelf. On a floured surface, knock the dough back by folding it inwards over and over again, until all the air is squeezed out. Split the dough into four to six equal-sized balls. Roll each ball into an oval shape, 3–5 mm thick. Remove the hot tray from the oven, dust with flour and place the pitta breads on it. You may have to cook them in batches. Bake for five to ten minutes, or until they start to colour. Remove them from the oven and cover with a clean cloth until cool.

HOMEMADE SPELT AND CHESTNUT BREAD

If you have gluten or yeast issues, omit the yeast and make a flatbread – just roll out the dough into thin pancakes and pan-fry for a minute each side.

100 g spelt flour
50 g chestnut flour
Pinch of sea salt

3 g dried yeast
100 ml cold water
1 tablespoon olive oil

Mix the flours and salt in a bowl. Add the yeast, if using, water and olive oil and knead into a smooth dough. Cover and leave to rest in the fridge for thirty minutes. Preheat the oven to 200°C. Take out the dough and knead again to get rid of any air. Bake for fifteen minutes.

HOMEMADE RYE-VITA

The proportions here depend on the size of your oven pan. Rolling the dough thinly takes practice – use a spatula rather than a rolling pin. You can also use spelt or other flours and change the seed mix or the oil. This is a great recipe for breakfast spreads.

100 g rye flour
20 ml grapeseed oil
20 ml water
10 g pumpkin seeds

10 g flax seeds
10 g sesame seeds
Sea salt

Set the oven to 180°C. In a large bowl mix the flour, oil and water into a ball. Add more water if it is too dry, making it workable without being overly dense. Lay a sheet of baking paper on your oven tray. Put the dough in the centre and, using a spatula, work it down to cover the whole tray about half a centimetre deep. Scatter the seeds on top and then the salt. Mark out the squares for your biscuits. Bake for forty minutes or until nicely golden. Take out and leave to cool, then break up the biscuits and store in a tin.

SALADS

The word salad has become shorthand for plain, boring green leaves. To be a great saladier you need to be a pirate in the supermarket, plundering small treasures to keep at home in the back of the larder, picking up interesting additions when you see them for the promise of future use.

A small salad as a starter for lunch or as part of a lunch box can be a miraculously inventive concoction. Lettuces are alkaline in themselves, containing vitamin C and beta carotenoids, and the white juices that flow from a cut stem contain lactucarium, a calming influence not too distantly related to opium (albeit in smaller quantities). Broadly speaking, the darker the leaves, the more nutritious. Making a salad colourful is almost a definition of making it richer in nutrients.

With the following three staple components you might already have a salad that includes some rocket leaves mixed with romaine, fresh thyme and walnut oil slaked with lemon. Add a few walnuts or a few pomegranate seeds (the permutations are endless around the seasons), or magically turn it into a chicken salad by adding a little mustard with the oil and some torn breast meat, and you have a fantastic lunch.

There will be other items in the kitchen, too, that will bring added texture – a few grains would be good, perhaps a spoonful of cooked vegetables from the vegetable tea or minestrone, a few stolen granola items destined for breakfast, a segment of grapefruit, a few sunflower seeds or some toasted almonds.

THE LEAF

From the crisp gem, romaine and iceberg to the bitter endives and chicories, and from the calming butterhead and bright red or yellow lollos to the peppery rocket and the cut-and-come-again varieties for window boxes, there are plenty of salad leaves to choose from. Aim to have two or three different kinds of lettuce to hand, perhaps one from each family, which can be pepped up with cress or sprouted beans.

THE HERBS

Fresh herbs are packed with goodness and salads provide a simple way to bring them into the diet. A little goes a long way, and one or two varieties will be enough. Thyme, of which there are a great many varieties, will pop up in spikes around the dish. A few leaves of hand-torn basil rivals lettuce for texture but is far more perfumed. Chopped flat and curly parsley or coriander also lend good texture and aroma.

THE DRESSING

Almond, walnut and pumpkin oils are all beautifully eloquent, but have strong flavours so should be diluted with olive oil. Some people like fruity olive oils or fiery, peppery varieties, but it is a good idea to have something more neutral in the cupboard, too. Grapeseed or any first pressing of sunflower or rapeseed are ideal.

Citrus juices or unpasteurised apple cider vinegar are best as acidifiers, as they have alkalising properties. Mustard is a great emulsifier for salad dressings – mustard seed is alkaline, and while the added vinegar is not, the fractional quantities you would consume mean that it is not something to be scared of. Homemade mayonnaise also needn't be avoided. Just be careful not to overdo any dressing. A little is enough and won't impact on the salad's nutrition.

How to make your own mayonnaise

Break a room-temperature egg yolk into a large bowl and add a good teaspoon of Dijon mustard. Use a wooden spoon to mix, and work rhythmically in one direction. With your spare hand, pour a few drops of good-quality vegetable oil into the bowl and continue to stir vigorously – always the same way - with the other. Keep adding the oil slowly, mixing to ensure the emulsion holds. As you work you will feel it getting thicker. Stir in a total of 100 ml of oil, and then a final 25 ml of extra-virgin olive oil to lend colour, character and flavour. Finally, add a splash of vinegar and, if you like it thinner, a splash of boiling water.

COMPOSED SALADS

Composed salads have fallen out of fashion but are an easy and excellent way to enjoy a wide variety of vegetables. Essentially, a composed salad may have some leaves, but is formed in large part from cooked vegetables. The alkaline cheat's way is to dress a bowl with two variations of salad leaves, skim off a few cooked vegetables from your minestrone as a base, and then dress it up.

Potatoes make good salads, especially in summer, as do green beans. Once you have a base, you can throw in some peas or broad beans or sweetcorn. Some couscous or farro would enjoy the company – even a little alkaline bread if there is enough dressing. A few pulses in the mix – small adzuki or lentils and a big one like chickpeas – would turn the salad into a main-course centrepiece.

You can cook all of these separately, but if you have shopped well and been cooking already, simply raid other parts of the kitchen to find elements that will come together as a brilliant large salad for no more effort perhaps than boiling an egg.

FRUIT SALADS

Fruit salads are easy and rewarding and always feel luxuriously healthy. A fine fruit salad can be built around three ingredients – melon, a citrus and an exotic fruit – all of which are alkaline and easy to digest. You could also add something small such as grapes or pomegranate seeds for extra appeal, or a smattering of passion fruit. Pomelo would also add a lovely fragrance. Any permutation works and can evolve into serial recipes. Try honeydew, kiwi and lime. Or Ogen melon, satsuma and pineapple.

The bigger fruit keep for a few days even after they are cut open. The fruits should be carved small and the salad is best chilled for half an hour or overnight before serving. The juice is also great on its own.

TEAS

Drinking herbal or vegetable teas throughout the day helps to ensure a steady intake of liquid and can aid sleep, re-energise the body and encourage digestion. Add a tablespoon of fresh, clean herbs or a teaspoon of dried herbs or grated root to a mug, top up with boiling water and let infuse for a few minutes before straining and drinking.

Try drinking a mug of hot water with a squeeze of lemon in the morning to get your digestion working and ready for breakfast. Calming teas can help you to unwind and prepare the body for sleep and a night recuperating from the day's activities.

Morning Teas
>> Rosemary – energises and promotes circulation and digestion
>> Ginger – soothes the stomach, reduces inflammation and eases stress
>> Thyme – relieves gas and congestion and acts as a diuretic
>> Sage – full of antioxidants
>> Peppermint – soothes the stomach and calms
>> Nettle – antiseptic and antimicrobial
>> Lemon verbena – calms the mind and aids digestion

Evening Teas
>> Lemon balm – calms the body and induces sleep
>> Yarrow – opens pores, increases circulation and relieves digestive complaints
>> Chamomile – antibacterial, soothes the stomach and relaxes mind and body
>> Fennel – eases digestion and acts as a diuretic

HOW TO MAKE HOMEMADE VEGETABLE TEA

This is an easy homemade vegetable tea that you can drink through the day, cold or hot as you prefer instead of black tea or coffee. One or two cups a day between meals can be something to look forward to. Often, hunger is more easily satisfied with readily digestible fluids than solids.

1 litre cold water
200 g celery
100 g carrot
100 g potato

Half a fennel bulb
Half a small broccoli stalk
Bunch of parsley and/or
lovage or rhubarb stalk

Put a the water on to boil in a big pan. Roughly trim and chop your vegetables into equal sizes – the skins have goodness in them so wash them rather than peel. Simmer for ten minutes. Add the herbs, cover and simmer for thirty minutes. Turn off the heat. Leave to cool and infuse for another ten minutes. Strain.

ALKALINE SPICE MIX

This spice mix can be added to your vegetable tea – simply add to the pot with the herbs. It is also a good addition to alkaline breads.

¼ teaspoon fennel seeds
¼ teaspoon coriander seeds
¼ teaspoon caraway seeds
¼ teaspoon juniper berries

¼ teaspoon thyme
1 bay leaf
¼ teaspoon grated root ginger
¼ teaspoon crushed garlic

Simply mix or grind together all of the ingredients and add to your tea or bread dough.

MAINTAINING A SPECIALIST DIET

There are a number of dietary allergies, intolerances and foods to avoid that are now so common that they need including here. Essentially, our bodies can only take so much of certain foods and when an overload occurs, the body starts to reject them. If you have allergies or intolerances, an alkaline diet is not only easy to follow, but can also help to relieve the irritation caused by certain foods.

Lactose and Dairy

As previously stated, dairy products are in essence acid-forming. They are also high in fat and cholesterol. On top of this, vital calcium, and that most readily absorbed by the body, can be readily found in leafy greens, beans, nuts and seeds. You can also substitute plant-based alternatives such as nut milks, but be careful as they often contain added sugars.

That being said, some fresh milk and non-aged cheeses can be beneficial and have a lower acidity than highly pasteurised products, which have lost most of their nutritional value. Opt for goat and sheep products, which are easier to digest and are more often found in their raw, unpasteurised state. Some dairy, such as probiotic yoghurt, also contains friendly microorganisms that benefit flora in the gut.

Gluten and Yeast

Spelt and rye are not strictly gluten-free, but are much easier to manage if eaten in small quantities. Completely gluten-free grains include corn, quinoa, millet, buckwheat and amaranth. Another allergy connected to gluten is yeast, which can be avoided by baking flatbreads and crackers, which are lighter and easier on the stomach.

Vegetarian and Vegan Diets

Animal proteins and dairy products, while present in many recipes, are not the focus of this diet. Because of this, cutting them out entirely or replacing with substitutes such as nut milks and soya is simple. A high intake of essential vitamins and minerals from vegetable sources means that deficiencies are easily avoided.

Sugar

We have become indoctrinated by the sugar industry. As products, sugars, fructose and sweeteners deliver zero nutrition and persuade us to eat things that we might not eat at all. While an alkaline diet should contain as little sugar as possible, we recognise that sweet things are enjoyable. We find sweetness in fruits and vegetables such as carrots and parsnips, and use natural alternatives such as stevia, honey or agave. While all added sweeteners are essentially acid-forming, agave has a low glycemic index, requires only a small amount to be used, and is generally easy to find.

Candida

We all carry small amounts of the yeast fungus candida in the mouth and intestine to help with digestion and nutrient absorption. However, too much sugar in the diet (and antibiotics that kill off friendly flora in the intestinal system) can lead to an overproduction, which causes havoc in the digestive system. An alkaline diet, low in sugars and carbohydrates, and an intake of probiotics such as live yoghurt will restore the natural candida balance. On top of this, gut flora thrive on high-fibre, nutrient-dense foods like fruits and vegetables.

Histamine

Histamine occurs in fermented foods, aged or preserved products such as Parmesan cheese and smoked meats, alcohol and nuts such as peanuts. Low levels of the enzyme diamine oxidase can cause an intolerance to these already acidic foods, which an alkaline diet will reduce or eliminate.

FREQUENTLY ASKED QUESTIONS

How strict should I be?

If you want to feel the full benefits of an alkaline diet, then try
to follow all the principles, which will inform your eating habits.
Remember that this is a lifestyle change, not a fad – find your own
patterns and let yourself enjoy becoming healthy again. An easy rule
is to stick with soups in the evening. A well-made soup can deliver
multiple vegetables and all the nourishment you might need.

Can I cook with olive oil or butter?

Olive oil and butter have valuable nutrients in them that are destroyed
when heated. Always add them at the very end of preparing your
meal, using a non-stick pan to cook with. Coconut oil is also a great
alternative to butter or oils, as it does not denature as quickly, meaning
that it is easier to digest and retains its many health benefits, but
plant-based oils are higher in Omega 3. Remember, oils and butter are
energy-dense and should be used sparingly.

How much is too much?

We all eat too much, probably because we like it and enjoy it. Rather
than denying ourselves, the point about an alkalising approach is to
maximise the pleasure. It actually takes about twenty minutes for the
stomach to send a message to the brain that it is full. So if you eat too
quickly, the stomach does not have time even to react. Mindful eating
will help you to eat smaller amounts naturally.

Is there anything I cannot eat?

You can eat anything, in moderation, but we try to cut down on
alcohol, meat and sugar, and eliminate as much processed food as
possible. An alkaline diet is about balance – the more different and
varied the sources of nutrients we get, the better. Plant is better than
animal, but it is about percentages not bans.

Is there anything I cannot drink?

Soft drinks are essentially just sugar, and should be avoided at all costs. Likewise coffee and black tea, because they are acid stimulants.

What about a glass of wine or beer?

If you want to take on the two-week cleanse in our first book, then a few weeks off might be smart but ordinarily there is no decree against a glass of wine. If it makes you feel better, have it, but try to go for a younger wine or organic preservative-free beer. In cooking, you can substitute apple juice, grape juice or a decent vegetable stock and you won't notice the difference anyway.

What is the problem with unripe fruit?

Unripe fruits are harder to digest and are less nutritionally valuable than their naturally ripe counterparts. This includes tomatoes – cooking helps to make tomatoes more alkaline, but when buying them, look for southern sun-drenched, happy tomatoes not northern hothouse imitations.

Why no pasta or rice?

Normal white rice and pasta deliver very little nutrition. They fill up your stomach, taking up space that could be occupied by something that is helping to make you healthy. However, as we have said before, it is all about balance and enjoyment. If you must have pasta or rice, choose wholegrain varieties that provide added fibre and don't overload them with oils or processed sauces.

How long before I notice any difference?

Eating alkaline foods can re-adjust your body quite quickly – a few days ought to be enough to show you the benefits. After a week you may well find that you have new energy and vitality again. We do not promise or even advocate weight loss as the focus of an alkaline diet, but it does occur in most people. The target should simply be to return to your body's natural size – something that the majority of us are not.

3
Spring

SPRING

Spring is the season of rebirth, and when the first buds begin to appear and the days get brighter, it is time to re-energise yourself and your surroundings. Take time to get outside, begin outdoor exercise and share garden lunches with friends and family. Open up the windows to your house, try a deep clean and bring in fresh flowers. You can also appreciate the bounteous produce available at this time of year — young vegetables are at their best and can be enjoyed raw or lightly steamed with fresh spring herbs.

START THE DAY
Spring nettle tonic 56

Radish juice 56

Mean green juice 57

Popeye juice 57

Curd with spring herbs 58

Curd with orange and radicchio 58

Original Bircher-Benner muesli 60

Papaya, pomelo and watermelon salad 60

Lemon and date hummus 61

Almond and carrot spread 61

*

SOUPS
Spring minestrone 62

Fennel and apple soup with parsley 64

Spring herb soup with watercress 64

SALADS

Salad of fresh cheese, raisins, pomegranate, walnuts and flaxseed 65

Watercress, apple and walnuts with a soured cream dressing 65

*

SMALL PLATES & SIDES

Courgettes with peas and curd 66

Courgettes with rosemary and curd 66

Boiled new potatoes with green sauce 69

Turnips with caraway and honey 69

Kale and purple sprouting broccoli 70

Steamed kohlrabi with chives 70

*

MAINS

Asparagus with turnips and gnocchi 72

Gnocchi with roast tomatoes and olive cream 73

Pan-fried salmon with cucumber and spinach 75

Fennel tapenade with sea bass 76

Salmon tartare with dill and chives 76

*

DESSERTS

Apple toast, warm goat's milk cheese and paprika 78

Pineapple carpaccio with chilli, mint and lime 78

Prunes and apricots stewed in sage tea with star anise 79

START THE DAY

Wild garlic leaves and nettles herald the beginning of spring.
Later, hedgerows fill with lovage. All of these leaves make
wonderful teas. Spring flowers can also be used to decorate
breakfast dishes.

SPRING NETTLE TONIC

*In old herbals, many less familiar plants were used as remedies and work
well in teas – burdock (root) for the body cells, dandelion for the kidneys and
liver and dock for the stomach. Use herbal remedies with caution, however,
as they can affect people in different ways. This variation, with nettle and
rosemary, was held to be good for the blood.*

1 sprig of nettle	1 slice of lemon
1 sprig of rosemary	250 ml water
5 slices of ginger root	Honey to taste

Bring the kettle to a near boil. Arrange the herbs in a glass and layer
the ginger and lemon on top. Pour on the almost boiled water.
Taste and season with a tip of a teaspoon of honey.

RADISH JUICE

*The leaves of radishes have more nutrients than the root itself.
They need to be garden-fresh or they discolour quickly.*

15 g radish leaves	250 ml cloudy apple juice
20 g radishes	1 tablespoon linseed oil
1 banana	Soda water
1 tablespoon lemon juice	

Wash the radish leaves well and pick out any that are discoloured. Peel
the banana. Blend together the leaves, radishes and banana. Add the
lemon juice, apple juice and linseed oil. Pour into a glass and top with
soda water.

POPEYE JUICE

Handful of spinach
1 apple
Half a courgette
1 banana
1 lime

5 mint leaves
250 ml coconut water
Water
Pinch of sea salt

Wash over the spinach. Core the apple. Chop the courgette. Peel the banana. Skin the lime. Add everything to a blender except the water and salt. Blitz. Taste, dilute with water and add the salt.

MEAN GREEN JUICE

2 celery stalks
2 cabbage leaves
4 romaine lettuce leaves
Half a cucumber

1 lemon
1 apple
Handful parsley
250 ml almond milk or water

Wash and roughly chop the celery, cabbage and romaine lettuce. Skin the cucumber and lemon. Core the apple. Blend everything together, adding more milk or water if you need it.

CURD WITH SPRING HERBS

If you cannot find curd, substitute a fresh, young goat's or sheep's milk cheese. This works well with more delicate herbs like chervil and the fronds of fennel – whatever's in season. You can serve on bread or with simple crudités of carrot and cucumber.

100 g fresh curd

Linseed or pumpkin oil

25 g fresh herbs – chives,
   parsley, chervil

10 g sesame seeds

1 teaspoon grated lemon
   or orange zest

Put the curd in a bowl and pour over the oil. Finely chop the herbs and fold into the curd. Sprinkle with sesame seeds and lemon zest. If you are serving this to others, you can also form the curd into balls and sprinkle over the herbs.

CURD WITH ORANGE AND RADICCHIO

This is very pretty and very neat. You can use ricotta instead of curd, if you like. Serve with crispbread to the side. If blood oranges are still around, their extra tartness will work, too.

50 g fresh curd

1 orange

Olive oil

1 radicchio leaf

10 g sesame seeds

Lightly mash the curd in a bowl. Peel the orange and remove three segments. Squeeze the rest for juice and add to the curd. Add a little olive oil and mash well. Spoon into the radicchio leaf and decorate with the three orange segments. Sprinkle with sesame seeds.

ORIGINAL BIRCHER-BENNER MUESLI

The original recipe from Dr Bircher-Benner in 1912 actually used condensed milk because of concerns about tuberculosis in fresh milk. That was before fridges were invented. It is interesting how simple this recipe is compared to today's busy granolas.

4 tablespoons rolled oats   Yoghurt
60 ml apple juice   1 apple
1 tablespoon lemon juice

Soak the oats in the apple and lemon juices overnight. In the morning, mix up with an equal amount of yoghurt. Grate in the apple at the last minute and mix well.

PAPAYA, POMELO AND WATERMELON SALAD

This will make more than a single portion, but the big fruits keep for a few days wrapped in cling film, so make just as much as you want. You can add other fruits if you have them; use grapefruit if you cannot find pomelo. The salad needs no sweetener and can double up as a lunchtime dessert.

50 g papaya   50 g watermelon
50 g pomelo

Get a big knife, a chopping board and a handsome bowl. Carve the papaya across and use a spoon to slip out the black pips. Cut off the skin and carve across, then down, to get neat chunks. For the pomelo, square off the skin and break open the fruit. You need to get rid of all the peel and pith, including the dividing membranes on each slice – it is best to work over the bowl so you catch all the juice. Once removed, add the segments to the salad. Carve the watermelon into thin triangles, remove the pips and criss-cross into sections. A lot of juice gathers around the watermelon – add it to the bowl. Stir the ingredients to combine.

ALMOND AND CARROT SPREAD

If you make your own almond milk, you can use the leftover pulp for this recipe. If you are using whole almonds, soak them overnight to make them easier to digest.

50 g ground almonds
100 g boiled carrots
1 tablespoon walnut oil
1 teaspoon sesame seeds

1 pinch of freshly grated
   ginger root
Rock or sea salt
1 tablespoon fresh coriander

Blend the almonds, carrots, walnut oil, sesame seeds and ginger in a food processor until very fine. Season with rock salt and the leaves of the fresh coriander.

LEMON AND DATE HUMMUS

This variation of hummus uses dates instead of chickpeas, which are slightly acid. Serve with grilled flatbread. You can also try this for lunch with salad.

1 lemon
6 dates

75 ml raw tahini

Peel the lemon and drop into a food processor. Take the stones out of the dates and add to the lemon. Spoon over the tahini and pulse.

SOUPS

The first green shoots of the year bring powerful chlorophylls and vitamins, and make strikingly colourful broths. Bright colour in fresh fruit and vegetables is always an indicator of antioxidants.

SPRING MINESTRONE

This staple herby minestrone uses early summer vegetables – vary the mix with whatever is in the market. Make sure you have roughly equal quantities. The base for the soup is a summer vegetable stock, and we have upped the quantities to make double – enough to freeze or eat throughout the week.

1.5 litres vegetable stock	2 garlic cloves
50 g fennel	50 g green beans
50 g asparagus	50 g peas
50 g potato	50 g broad beans
1 bunch spring onions	Sea salt
50 g cauliflower	Black pepper
50 g broccoli	Small handful of fresh chives
50 g courgettes	

Bring the stock to the boil in a big pan as you prepare the vegetables. Wash the fennel, asparagus, potato and spring onions, cut into equal sizes and add to the pan. Break the cauliflower and broccoli into bite-sized florets and add. Dice the courgette and finely slice the garlic and green beans. Pod the peas and broad beans and add to the pan with the other vegetables. Season and simmer for about twenty minutes. Snip the chives over the top.

FENNEL AND APPLE SOUP WITH PARSLEY

The apple gives a nice twist here, but be careful that the juice is not too strong and, obviously, that it has not been artificially sweetened.

300 g fennel

80 g floury potatoes

500 ml vegetable stock
or water

250 ml apple juice

30 g spring onions

2 tablespoons double cream

1 tablespoon fennel seeds

4 sprigs of fennel

Wash the fennel and potatoes and chop into small cubes. Bring the stock and apple juice to a simmer, add the fennel and potatoes and cook for fifteen minutes. Chop the spring onions and add for the last five minutes of cooking. Take off the heat and blend with the double cream. Garnish with the fennel seeds and sprigs of fennel.

SPRING HERB SOUP WITH WATERCRESS

You can make this soup all the year round, simply by varying the herbs as they come into season. It is especially welcome in spring, however, when the first shoots are coming through. Sorrel, wild garlic, even nettles – they all work well. Watercress adds a pepperiness. Later in the year you might use parsley or even something as delicate as chervil.

400 g floury potatoes

750 ml vegetable stock
or water

50 g spring onions

100 g watercress

50 g fresh spring herbs

Sea salt to taste

60 ml yoghurt

Wash and chop the potatoes and boil for fifteen minutes in the vegetable stock. Chop the spring onions, add to the potatoes and cook for a couple of minutes more. Remove from the heat and throw in the watercress and the herbs. Blend and add the salt. Serve with a spoon of yoghurt.

SALADS

A salad doesn't have to be just a few crispy leaves of lettuce. You can make use of lots of interesting and nutritious foods from the market. A salad can even be a main dish in its own right.

SALAD OF FRESH CHEESE, RAISINS, POMEGRANATE, WALNUTS AND FLAXSEED

10 g raisins	10 g pomegranate seeds
Water or grapefruit juice	Flaxseed or pumpkin oil
100 g fresh young goat's milk cheese	Sprig of mint
	Sea salt
20 g walnuts	Black pepper
10 g flaxseeds	

Soak the raisins in water or grapefruit juice. Leave for half an hour or overnight to plump up. In a bowl, break up the fresh goat's cheese with a fork. Break up the walnuts into small pieces and add to the cheese. Add the flaxseeds and pomegranate seeds. Dress with a tablespoon of flaxseed or pumpkin oil. Tear off the mint leaves and add to the bowl. Toss well. Season with sea salt and a grind of black pepper.

WATERCRESS, APPLE AND WALNUTS WITH A SOURED CREAM DRESSING

Handful of watercress	1 lime
6 romaine salad leaves	20 g soured cream
1 apple	Pumpkin oil
25 g walnuts	

Pick over the watercress and mix in with the other leaves. Chop the apple, skin on, into cubes and add to the mix. Crush the walnuts into small pieces and add. Squeeze over the juice of the lime. Add the soured cream and the pumpkin oil. Mix well.

SMALL PLATES & SIDES

Spring vegetables need only a drizzle of nut oil or a little butter, but spices, herby sauces or a little cheese are delicious too.

COURGETTES WITH PEAS AND CURD

100 g courgettes	Olive oil
Vegetable stock	Fennel fronds
50 g peas	2 tablespoons curd
Lettuce leaves	

Slice the courgettes into ribbons. Steam in vegetable stock for three minutes. Add the peas and cook for three minutes more – the courgettes should be just collapsing. Drain off the stock and put the courgettes and peas in a bowl with the lettuce leaves. Dress with olive oil and fennel fronds. Spoon on the curd.

COURGETTES WITH ROSEMARY AND CURD

One-quarter of a courgette	Quarter of a lemon
200 ml water	1 flatbread or crispbread
2 tablespoons chives	Fresh soft goat's milk cheese
Sprig of rosemary	or curd, to cover
1 teaspoon fennel seeds	1 tablespoon olive oil

Thinly slice the courgette and pan-fry for one minute to colour. Add the water, cover and cook for three minutes. Add the herbs, fennel seeds and juice of the lemon. Cook for one minute, to fuse the flavours. Using a slotted spoon, remove the courgette but keep the liquid bubbling. Cover the flatbread with the goat's cheese and layer over the courgettes. Finish the sauce by adding the olive oil off the heat. Use a teaspoon to dribble a little sauce over the courgette – be sure to pick up the little fennel seeds.

5 WAYS WITH CARROTS

The carrot has spectacular health benefits as an antioxidant and cardiovascular stimulant. Humble, cheap and readily available all year, the carrot is a superstar superfood. Steaming is better than boiling, especially for younger carrots. They can mash, too, which surprises people, and they combine well with other vegetables – from onions to celeriac to Brussels sprouts. Dill and parsley both go well with carrots.

>> An indespensible source of sweetness in stocks and broths, the carrot stars in its own soup, with orange, for a 1970s classic. Another way to pair the two is to steam the carrots for ten minutes and then drain and roast with orange, rosemary and garlic for a further ten minutes.

>> Grated as a salad, carrot is a useful standby. Make the salad more glamorous by mixing in some currants that have been soaked in the juice of an orange and dressed with olive oil.

>> Pair carrot with daikon, which is also very alkaline. Shave both into thin slivers and rest in water for fifteen minutes. Make a dressing with the juice of a lime, a grating of ginger and a teaspoon of toasted sesame seeds. Garnish with coriander.

>> Alongside potatoes and peas, carrots are a key component in a Russian salad. Mix with your homemade alkaline mayonnaise (see page 43).

>> Or forget the cooking, and eat your carrots raw as snacks. As crudités they go well with cucumber batons served with spreads and dips such as hummus or guacamole.

BOILED NEW POTATOES WITH GREEN SAUCE

This sauce also works well with cold meats or a grilled lamb chop, so save any leftovers in the fridge.

4 new potatoes

100 g mixed spring herbs –
parsley, chives, cress, sorrel,
chervil, borage

120 g soured cream

50 g mayonnaise

2 tablespoons mustard

Half a lemon

2 free-range eggs, boiled

20 g onion

Sea salt

Black pepper

Place the new potatoes on to boil for fifteen minutes. Finely chop all the herbs and mix in the soured cream and mayonnaise. Add the mustard and the juice of the lemon. Dice the eggs and the onion and fold in. Zest the lemon and sprinkle over. You should have the consistency of mayonnaise. If it is too thick, dilute with a tablespoon or two of vegetable stock. Season with salt and pepper. Drain the potatoes and leave to cool for ten minutes before dressing with a tablespoon of the sauce.

TURNIPS WITH CARAWAY AND HONEY

Turnips can handle quite strong flavours. They go well with veal and pork (and with red wine), and can also be baked with a stuffing of millet or farro for forty minutes.

100 g turnip

1 teaspoon caraway or
dill seeds

1 tablespoon honey

1 teaspoon rock salt

Trim and dice the turnip into 5-mm slices. Steam for five minutes with the caraway or dill seeds. Drain and return to the pan. Pour over the honey and salt and toss well.

KALE AND PURPLE SPROUTING BROCCOLI

Young broccoli hardly needs anything except a little butter.

100 g purple sprouting broccoli	100 g kale
	1 tablespoon butter

Put a kettle on to boil. Trim the stalk at the base of each broccoli stem so they are all the same size. Cut out the central stalks on the kale and use scissors to snip the leaves into small dice. Lay the kale in a pan, with the broccoli on top. Pour over enough water to cover the base of the pan and steam, covered, for five minutes. The vegetables will be well coloured and just getting limp. Drain. Add the butter and turn into a serving dish. Serve as it is or with grilled or roasted meats.

STEAMED KOHLRABI WITH CHIVES

When kohlrabi is young, they do not need to be peeled. You can mix purple and green for visual effect.

1 kohlrabi	1 tablespoon chives
1 tablespoon butter	Sea salt
1 tablespoon lemon juice	Black pepper

Peel the kohlrabi if it is not young and pliant. Slice into rounds, no thicker than your finger. Steam for ten minutes. Serve with the butter and lemon juice. Scissor over the chives and be generous with the salt and pepper.

MAINS

Spring always seems to come late from a kitchen point of view – make the most of new-season potatoes, asparagus, purple sprouting broccoli and herbs when serving proteins.

ASPARAGUS WITH TURNIPS AND GNOCCHI

Make the gnocchi in advance – they will keep. If you make too many, they freeze well. Bake the potatoes and fill the skins with soured cream and chives (see page 159). The potato needs to be warm for making gnocchi.

1 large potato	2 fat white asparagus
150 g spelt flour	1 handful fresh spinach
Vegetable stock	Butter
1 turnip	Paprika
3 fat green asparagus	

Bake the potato for an hour, or until cooked. Spoon out the flesh on to a well-floured surface. Knead the potato and flour together – it may feel a bit difficult at first, but will soon transform into a flexible dough. Roll the dough out flat and cut into narrow strips. Use the palm of your hand to roll each strip into a sausage shape, then pinch off pieces about the size of the top of your thumb. Set aside.

Bring a pan of the vegetable stock to the boil. Skin and slice the turnip and cook for seven minutes. Snap off the bases of the asparagus and add to the stock. They will cook in about the same time. Lift the vegetables out of the stock and drain.

Drop a few gnocchi at a time into the same stock – they need plenty of room. They will drop to the bottom and then rise up and float. Cook for thirty seconds or so once they have risen, then lift out

To serve, line a salad bowl with the spinach leaves and layer with the turnip, then the asparagus. Dress the gnocchi with butter and paprika and add to the bowl.

GNOCCHI WITH ROAST TOMATOES AND OLIVE CREAM

Instead of making the olive cream for this recipe, you can use the fennel tapenade from page 76, if you have any left.

10 small ripe tomatoes
10 black olives, pitted
1 tablespoon olive oil
10 gnocchi (see opposite)

Handful of spinach leaves
1 tablespoon butter
Sprig of basil

Turn the oven to medium and roast the tomatoes for ten minutes. Make your olive cream: blend the olives with olive oil to form a smooth emulsion. Bring a pan of water to the boil and drop in the gnocchi. Cook for two minutes, then drain. Line a bowl with the spinach leaves and arrange the gnocchi and roasted tomatoes on top. Pour over the olive cream and add the butter. Garnish with basil.

5 WAYS WITH BROCCOLI

Studies have revealed that just 100 g of broccoli provides an adult's recommended daily intake of vitamin C. It also has higher levels of carotenoids than any other brassica and is rich in lutein, which has spawned a raft of research around its impact on the immune system and potential cancer defences. Boiling broccoli reduces the levels of anti-carcinogenics noticeably – it only needs to steam for three to four minutes.

>> In spring, varieties like purple sprouting broccoli are to be savoured just as much as asparagus and can be dressed simply with butter. Like asparagus, it does not really need too much work, although it does like strong flavours…

>> Steamed broccoli florets mingle well with curried mayonnaise as bites. Just add a teaspoon of curry spices to your mayonnaise or a grating of fresh ginger root and turmeric if you have it. Or try a powerful romesco sauce (see page 103).

>> In salads, broccoli works well with roasted red peppers, toasted pine nuts or almonds and a dressing of mustard butter with diced shallots and lemon. Or try broccoli with farro, toasted almonds and chilli, dicing up a fresh peach into the salad as dressing.

>> Broccoli makes a very quick soup poached for five minutes in vegetable stock and then liquidized with a little yoghurt or cream to smooth. Add a teaspoon of mustard for a little kick.

>> Stir-fried with a little coconut oil, broccoli will stand up to garlic and chilli and a dressing of soy, sesame and lime.

PAN-FRIED SALMON WITH CUCUMBER AND SPINACH

Large handful of spinach
1 tablespoon butter
75 g salmon fillet
40 g cucumber

Sprig of parsley
Carrot and parsnip sauce
  (see below)

Wash the spinach and put in a large pan. Heat for about two minutes. As it wilts, it cooks in its own juices. Drain the spinach and squeeze all the water out of it, pressing two or three times to make it as dry as possible. Add the butter. Pan-fry the salmon in a nonstick pan for three or four minutes each side. Meanwhile, slice the cucumber thinly and make a bed on the serving plate. Serve the salmon on the cucumber, with the spinach to the side, and pour over the sauce. Garnish with parsley.

Carrot and parsnip sauce

200 g carrots
200 g parsnips
40 g fennel plus
  leaves for garnish

Vegetable stock
1 tablespoon cream
1 tablespoon butter

Wash and peel the vegetables. Roughly chop and cook in vegetable stock for twenty minutes, until soft. Drain and keep back the liquid for stock. Blend the vegetables for two minutes, then strain through a sieve. Add the cream and adjust the consistency. To serve warm, add the butter and the fennel leaves at the last minute.

FENNEL TAPENADE WITH SEA BASS

If cooking for three or four people, buy a whole fish. Sea bass is best baked in foil, or in a flour-and-water crust layered with herbs and salt. The fish is cooked when the crust hardens. This tapenade could also work well with roasted vegetables such as peppers, and some chickpeas too.

75 g black olives, pitted	2 garlic cloves
75 g green olives, pitted	1 lemon
Half a fennel bulb	Olive oil
2 tablespoons fresh thyme	70 g sea bass fillet

Put the olives in a food processor. Roughly chop the fennel and add that. Pick the leaves off the thyme – no stalks – and add those. Peel the garlic and add that. Peel the lemon and add whole. Add a good slug of olive oil and pulse. Check for consistency and add more oil if you like. Leave to infuse. Grill or pan-fry the sea bass for four minutes each side, or bake whole in the oven for twenty-five minutes. Serve with the tapenade, spinach, new-season carrots and steamed potatoes.

SALMON TARTARE WITH DILL AND CHIVES

This little treat is designed to get more herbs into the diet. You need sashimi-fresh fish. Mackerel, tuna and trout can also work but must be very fresh for the best results.

50 g salmon fillet	1 tablespoon yoghurt
Half a lemon	1 teaspoon Dijon mustard
10 g dill and chives	10 g rocket, or spelt bread

Dice the salmon fillet into small cubes. Squeeze over a few drops of lemon. Chop the herbs finely and mix with the yoghurt and mustard. Fold the mix into the salmon. Serve on the rocket as a salad base or on toasted spelt bread.

DESSERTS

Sweet dishes and desserts can be an afterthought at this time of year, but simple fruits will provide a nutritious and interesting end to lunch or early dinner.

APPLE TOAST, WARM GOAT'S MILK CHEESE AND PAPRIKA

1 apple
50 g fresh goat's milk cheese

1 tablespoon double cream
1 teaspoon paprika

Cut the apple across the centre to get a slice about 1 cm thick, and cut out the core. Cover the apple with a good smear of the goat's cheese. Grill for two minutes. Add the double cream and return to the grill for thirty seconds. Sprinkle with the paprika.

PINEAPPLE CARPACCIO WITH CHILLI, MINT AND LIME

This is a really fresh-tasting, refreshing dessert. Pineapple will keep for a few days if you slice it across and seal with cling film. You can vary the seasonings to ring the changes. Vanilla works well, for example.

1 slice of pineapple
1 red chilli

1 lime
Handful of mint

Cut a 2-cm thick slice from the pineapple. Carve off the skin. Slice as thinly as possible onto a plate, cutting out the core as you go. Finely dice the chilli, removing the seeds. In a bowl, mix the chilli with the juice of the lime. Rough-chop the mint and add to the bowl. Pour the sauce over the pineapple and leave to infuse for five minutes.

PRUNES AND APRICOTS STEWED IN SAGE TEA WITH STAR ANISE

This is a twist on the French classic of prunes and Armagnac. Apricots are also alkaline and give the dish lustre and a sense of luxury. The star anise adds a little of the exotic.

100 g prunes
100 g dried apricots
1 star anise

1 tablespoon dried sage
Yoghurt, to serve

Boil a kettle of water. Put the prunes and dried apricots in a big bowl with the star anise and sage. Pour over the water and steep for one hour. Transfer to the fridge overnight. Serve with yoghurt.

4
Summer

SUMMER

Summer is a time to rejoice – longer days and warm evenings that can be enjoyed through lazy dinners and good conversation, a time for holidays, relaxation and the restorative effects of bright sunlight warming our skin. Use this time to unwind. Walk to or from work, and spend time with your thoughts, enjoying the sights, sounds and smells around you. A desire for light, fresh meals will mean that ripe fruits, salads and chilled soups become go-to recipes for alkaline living.

SALADS

A really big cooked alkaline salad 93
Warm vegetable salad with polenta and red pepper sauce 94
Salad of kohlrabi, carrot, and courgette with coriander 94

*

SMALL PLATES & SIDES

Roast pepper and almond tzatziki 95
Kohlrabi and avocado slaw 97
Salad of sprouts, fennel, carrot, apple, and mango 97
Chilled herb and raisin ragout 98
Grilled fennel with black olives 98
Celeriac, herb and courgette cakes 99

*

MAINS

Lettuce wraps with chicken and sesame 100
Lemon salsa with monkfish ceviche 101
Grilled red mullet with parsley sauce 101
Roast chicken with romesco sauce 103
Thai-style green curry 104
Mashed broad beans and mint with lamb chops 105

*

DESSERTS

Fresh figs with yoghurt and honey 107
Baked peaches with honey and almonds 107
Summer pudding 109

START THE DAY

Remember, the best way to start the day is with a glass of warm water. If you like, you can add a few drops of lemon, orange or grapefruit juice. Then give your body half an hour to prepare before breakfast.

RED PUNCH

Smoothies are best drunk cool, so keep the fruit in the fridge for an hour before starting.

Handful of tender
  beetroot leaves
1 red pepper

1 slice of watermelon
12 large strawberries
250 ml water

Wash the beetroot leaves and chop the pepper. Throw in the blender with the watermelon and strawberries. You can remove the pips from the watermelon, although they will fall to the bottom of the glass anyway. Pour in the water and blend.

PAPAYA AND YOGHURT SMOOTHIE

15 g walnuts
2 tablespoons linseeds
200 g yoghurt
2 tablespoons linseed oil

1 teaspoon agave syrup
Lemon or orange juice
100 g papaya

Grind the walnuts and linseeds in a small coffee grinder or a pestle and mortar. Do not grind them too fine. Put them into a glass bowl with the yoghurt, linseed oil and agave syrup. Stir and season with a squeeze of fresh lemon or orange juice. Peel the papaya, dice it and lay on top.

MOJITO FRUIT SALAD

Mojito does not have to be a drink, or even have alcohol. This salad packs its own pick-me-up punch. This recipe will make enough to last a couple of days, and will benefit from chilling overnight anyway. The rest of the whole fruits can be stored in the fridge.

100 g watermelon   3 limes
2 ripe mangoes   Bunch of mint
100 g pineapple

Slice the watermelon, mangoes and pineapple into equal sizes, taking care to keep the juice. Add the zest and juice of the limes. Arrange the fruit on a plate, pour over the juice and decorate with mint.

STRAWBERRY AND PEACH COMPOTE

One of the great luxuries of summer is when strawberries and peaches overlap for a few weeks. Try other fruits, too – raspberries or the first blackberries – but make sure the peach dominates. White flesh peaches are even more special and nectarines can also work. Work over a bowl to catch all the juices.

1 ripe peach
6 strawberries

Slice the peach in half and slip out the stone. Cut across and lengthwise to get neat dice. Wash and trim the strawberries and quarter them. Mix all together and leave to infuse for five minutes.

FENNEL, CUCUMBER, ORANGE, GRAPEFRUIT AND FIG SALAD

This is a lovely arrangement of summer alkaline fruits – you want equal quantities of each in your salad.

1 fennel bulb

Half a cucumber

1 orange

1 grapefruit

1 fig

Remove any damaged outer leaves from the fennel and cut in half. Slice across into batons. Peel the cucumber and dice into batons. Peel and de-pith the orange and the grapefruit. Hold a couple of segments back to squeeze over the juice as dressing. Quarter the fig. Arrange the salad and dress with orange and grapefruit juice.

ENERGY BARS

If you are active or doing sports, these high-value bars pack a lot of portable nutrition into a small place. You can purée any fresh fruit you like for this recipe, which will yield about eight bars.

100 g cooked buckwheat

125 g fruit purée –
    strawberries, raspberries

200 g fresh dates

40 g almonds

60 g blueberries

30 g honey

30 g linseeds

30 g sesame seeds

1 lemon

Place the buckwheat and the fruit purée in a food processor and add the dates, the almonds, blueberries, honey, linseeds and sesame seeds. Take the zest off the lemon with a sharp knife. Juice the rest of the lemon and add to the processor with the zest. Process to mix thoroughly and fashion into portable bars. Wrap in cling film to store.

FRUIT AND NUT SNACK

Make as much of this as you like – it looks pretty as an extra dish at breakfast or lunchtime, but you can also take it with you to the office as a snack. Add spices or chilli if you like. It will keep through the week.

20 g walnuts

20 g almonds

20 g pumpkin seeds

20 g flaxseeds

20 g sesame seeds

20 g dried cranberries

20 g raisins

Break up the nuts lightly with a pestle and mortar. Mix in the seeds and the fruit. Stir well.

ROAST GARLIC ON TOAST

There will be fresh garlic in the market. You need a large bulb with fat cloves. Garlic itself is alkaline and this makes a pungent open sandwich. Serve with a parsley salad.

1 fresh garlic bulb

1 slice of sourdough bread

1 tablespoon olive oil

Sprig of parsley

Roast the garlic whole in a medium oven for approximately forty minutes, until the cloves are soft. Remove and leave to cool for one minute while you toast the sourdough. Separate the cloves and squeeze the soft flesh on to the toast – enough to cover. Drizzle with a little olive oil and garnish with chopped parsley.

TAHINI WITH SPROUTS ON FLATBREAD

This is an alkaline variation on hummus, with just tahini as its base. It is delicious served on homemade flatbread. The trick here is to get the right texture.

4 tablespoons tahini

3 tablespoons cider vinegar

2 spring onions

1 lemon, juice only

1 garlic clove

2 tablespoons fresh herbs

125 ml water

Sea salt

125 ml olive oil

4 tablespoons sprouted beans

Flatbread or crispbread

Place everything except the olive oil, sprouted beans and flatbread in a blender, and blitz. Add the oil, as if making mayonnaise, and blend to a hummus-like cream. Spread the cream on flatbread, garnished with the sprouted beans.

SOUPS

Soups don't always have to be served warm. On hot summer days a chilled soup can be delicious, nutritious and refreshing.

CUCUMBER, GARLIC AND MINT SOUP

This is an alkalising summer tonic. It is very quick to make, but give yourself enough time to let it settle and chill in the fridge.

2 cucumbers	3 garlic cloves
Sea salt	Black pepper
400 ml vegetable stock	Half a lemon
150 ml yoghurt	Bunch of fresh mint
150 ml double cream	Olive oil, for drizzling

Peel the cucumbers, cut in half lengthwise and scoop out the seeds with a teaspoon. Slice the flesh horizontally, place on a flat plate and sprinkle with sea salt. Leave for fifteen minutes, then rinse and squeeze off any excess water. Put the stock, yoghurt, cream and cucumber in a blender. Peel the garlic, add to the blender and blend. Season with salt, pepper and lemon juice to taste. Throw in the mint and blend one last time. Chill in the fridge for fifteen minutes. Serve with a drizzle of olive oil.

WATERMELON GAZPACHO

500 g watermelon	2 teaspoons sea salt
200 g almonds	3 slices of firm bread
3 garlic cloves	200 g ice cubes
2 tablespoons orange juice	1 tablespoon olive oil

Keep about one-third of the watermelon back for later and purée the rest in a blender. Push it through a sieve to get rid of the pips. Return to the blender with the almonds, peeled garlic, orange juice and salt. Blend again. To serve, shred the bread, carve the leftover watermelon into small wedges and pour the juice over the top. Add the ice cubes and olive oil.

GREEN GAZPACHO

You can vary this using any green herbs, or even asparagus. The more varied the mix, the more interesting the soup. If you don't have any vegetable stock, you can use the water from the potato and increase the amount of cream.

50 g potato	2 spring onions
50 g mixed herbs – parsley, chives, cress, sorrel, chervil	750 ml vegetable stock
	100 g soured cream
25 g spinach	Half a lemon

Wash the potato and chop small. Boil until soft, about twelve minutes. Put everything except the soured cream and lemon into a blender and purée. Add the soured cream and a squeeze of lemon juice. Purée once more. Chill in the fridge and serve cold, in glasses.

5 WAYS WITH FENNEL

Botanically, fennel belongs to the Umbelliferae family and is related to parsley, carrots, dill and coriander. It is high in vitamin C, fibre, folate and potassium. Fennel is more versatile than it seems, working equally well raw, poached or roasted and braised with apple juice for forty minutes. It is an almost essential ingredient in an alkaline tea (see page 47) or stock, and as a soup, either on its own or with leeks.

» The little wispy leaves at the top of a fennel bulb are lovely in their own right for garnishing and peppering up other herbs. They also love oil and lemon – see roasting, below.

» Fennel makes an interesting salad sliced thinly – virtually shaved off a grater – with beetroot and apple. For smoked fish, such as trout, dress the salad with yoghurt and horseradish. For a simpler salad, just add orange, poppy seeds and rocket with a little nut oil.

» Fennel seeds can be rubbed into meat – especially pork – for grilling. Grate the bulb into a coleslaw with celeriac, mustard and mayonnaise for an accompaniment.

» Fennel can be roasted in the oven or cut into slices and cooked on a griddle or barbecue. It marries well with a marinade of diced black olives, crushed garlic, lemon, oil and its fronds. Leave the hot fennel in this mix for five minutes before serving.

» Try fennel in a salsa with cucumber, avocado, red onion, coriander, lemon and black pepper.

SALADS

These larger salads are great to share, and as the vegetables are cooked, they can also be enjoyed for evening meals. A beautiful, bright plate of vegetables that everyone can dig into is a great dinner party staple.

A REALLY BIG COOKED ALKALINE SALAD

A good salad is a memorable thing. This is a cooked variation of caponata, a Sicilian variation on ratatouille. It is a slow cook, but rewarding, and works better made in bigger quantities like this, then stored in the fridge to let the flavours develop over time. You need a big wide pan.

1 large onion	1 large courgette
3–4 celery stalks, including leaves	55 g tomato purée
	20 green olives, pitted
1 carrot	3 tablespoons pine nuts
1 kg aubergine	5 tablespoons olive oil

Chop the onion, celery and carrot into thumb-sized chunks. Use them to layer the base of a pan and add just enough water to cover them. Bring to a simmer. Chop the aubergine and courgette into equal sizes and lay in the pan. Add the tomato purée, cover and leave to simmer for twenty to thirty minutes so the vegetables are breaking down, but not mush. Add the olives, pine nuts and a good measure of olive oil. You can eat this as it is, served on toast for a hearty lunch, but it is also good cold on warm summer evenings.

WARM VEGETABLE SALAD WITH POLENTA AND RED PEPPER SAUCE

Composed salads – salads made up of cooked vegetables – allow lots of vegetables into the diet as well as other elements, such as nut oils and soured cream or yoghurt for dressings. This salad works in a sort of upside-down way but is very satisfying. It is great for sharing, and will serve four people.

100 g red peppers	75 g fennel
Olive oil	75 g carrots
200 g polenta	75 g courgette
400 g vegetable stock	75 g asparagus
75 g broccoli	Sprig of basil

First make the sauce: roast the whole red peppers in a medium oven for thirty minutes, until they start to collapse. Take them out of the oven and leave in a sealed plastic bag for twenty minutes. This makes them easier to peel. Peel and blend with a little oil, if needed.

Next make the polenta: pour slowly into the hot vegetable stock. Stir well and remove from the heat.

Wash all the other vegetables and chop into equal sizes, as needed. Steam for ten minutes, drain and keep back the water for stock. To serve, make a base of the polenta, lay the vegetables on top and pour the red pepper sauce on top of that. Garnish with basil.

SALAD OF KOHLRABI, CARROT, AND COURGETTE WITH CORIANDER

Vegetable stock or water	100 g courgette
100 g kohlrabi	4 tablespoons coriander,
100 g carrot	chervil or mixed herbs

Bring a pan of vegetable stock or water to the boil. Wash and grate or slice the kohlrabi and the carrot so they are equal-sized ribbons. Poach the vegetables for five minutes. Dice the courgette and add for the last two minutes of cooking. Drain well, keeping the water for stock. Chop the herbs. Combine and serve.

SMALL PLATES & SIDES

When the weather is hot, your body instinctively needs less food as you are not using up as much energy trying to keep warm. Light dishes and dips using cool yoghurt are an easy way to end the day.

ROAST PEPPER AND ALMOND TZATZIKI

Traditional Greek tzatziki is a superbly alkaline mix of yoghurt, garlic and cucumber. If you travel north to Bulgaria, you might find it expanded with parsley, almonds and roasted peppers like this recipe. This is also a great dish to make ahead and keep in the fridge for a quick lunch or supper – store any leftovers from this recipe for up to two days.

2 large red peppers
2 large cucumbers
2 tablespoons sea salt, plus
    extra for seasoning
10 almonds
350 g Greek yoghurt

2–3 tablespoons lemon juice
Olive oil
4 garlic cloves
Bunch of parsley
Black pepper

Place the peppers in a medium oven and roast for thirty minutes, until they collapse. Remove and keep in a sealed plastic bag for twenty minutes to make them easier to peel. While the peppers are cooking, thinly grate the cucumber and cover with the salt. Leave for fifteen minutes. Wash the salt off the cucumber and squeeze out all the juice. Toast the almonds and crush them in a pestle and mortar.

  Peel the peppers, chop finely and fold into the yoghurt. Add in the cucumber and mix well. Add the lemon juice, crushed almonds and olive oil. Crush and dice the garlic and add to the mix. Finely chop the parsley and mix in. Leave to infuse the flavours for at least thirty minutes. Season to taste. Eat with freshly grilled flatbread.

KOHLRABI AND AVOCADO SLAW

1 kohlrabi

2 tablespoons lemon juice

1 avocado, sliced

120 g soured cream
  or yoghurt

2 tablespoons olive oil

5 tablespoons fresh herbs
  – tarragon, parsley, chervil,
  thyme, chives

Grate the kohlrabi or cut finely into matchsticks. Sprinkle over the lemon juice. In another bowl mix the avocado, soured cream, olive oil and chopped herbs, keeping a few back for garnish. Combine with the kohlrabi and decorate with a few herb sprigs.

SALAD OF SPROUTS, FENNEL, CARROT, APPLE, AND MANGO

This is a fantastic salad to eat on a hot day, and will keep well in the fridge overnight too.

75 g carrots

75 g fennel

75 g celery

100 g bean sprouts

50 g apple

50 g mango

2 tablespoons linseed oil

Handful sunflower seeds

1 lime

Basil

Chop the carrot, fennel and celery into equal sizes and steam for ten minutes. Drain and cool, and mix in with the bean sprouts. Dice the apple and mango and toss in the bowl. Dress with the linseed oil, sunflower seeds and a good squeeze of lime juice. Top with basil leaves.

CHILLED HERB AND RAISIN RAGOUT

3 tablespoons dried raisins	2 garlic cloves
125 ml apple juice	1 tablespoon fresh mint
1 cucumber	1 tablespoon fresh tarragon
Rock salt	Black pepper
100 ml yoghurt	

Soak the raisins for an hour or overnight in apple juice. Wash and grate the cucumber into a bowl. Sprinkle with salt and leave for fifteen minutes, then wring out all the juices. Mix in with the yoghurt. Crush the garlic and chop the herbs. Add to the yoghurt, along with the raisins. Mix well. Season with black pepper and rock salt. Serve with grilled flatbread.

GRILLED FENNEL WITH BLACK OLIVES

This is a brilliant vegetarian recipe for summertime barbecues.

1 fennel bulb	1 lemon
5 tablespoons kalamata olives	Parsley
2 garlic cloves	Basil
1 tablespoon olive oil	

Slice the fennel into 1-cm slices. Grill on a griddle or barbecue – five minutes each side or until well coloured but not quite burned

Make the dressing. Dice the olives, crush the garlic, mix in the oil and juice of the lemon and chop and add the herbs. Lay the warm fennel in the dressing and allow at least five minutes to macerate. Serve warm or cold.

CELERIAC, HERB AND COURGETTE CAKES

50 g celeriac	Flour
50 g courgette	Coconut oil
100 g mashed cooked potato	1 garlic clove
20 g fresh herbs	120 ml yoghurt
Sea salt	120 g soured cream
Black pepper	Handful of dill

Grate the celeriac and courgette into the mashed potato. Chop the herbs finely and add to the mix with sea salt and black pepper. Fashion into little cakes and sprinkle over a little flour. Put in the fridge for one hour to chill. Add a little coconut oil to a solid frying pan and heat. Fry the patties quickly on both sides to brown.

Crush the garlic in a pestle and mortar and work in a little salt. Add the yoghurt and soured cream. Chop the dill finely and mix in well. Serve with the freshly cooked patties.

MAINS

Fresh fish, complex spices and aromatic herbs match our summer dishes to the feeling of the season – liveliness, excitement and maybe the desire to try something new.

LETTUCE WRAPS WITH CHICKEN AND SESAME

This is easy to make and a splendid way to use fresh herbs – vary them depending on what you have in season. If you would like a vegetarian option, replace the chicken with tofu or even simply more vegetables, such as edamame, bean sprouts, grated carrot and daikon.

75 g chicken breast	2 tablespoons sesame oil
Half a cucumber	1 lime
1 spring onion	2 teaspoons honey
Handful of coriander	Sea salt
2 romaine lettuce leaves	2 tablespoons sesame seeds
5 tablespoons olive oil	

Poach the chicken for about fourteen minutes. Lift out and leave to rest and cool. Skin the cucumber and slice thinly, cut the spring onion horizontally into little discs and chop the coriander. Spoon the vegetables and coriander into the lettuce leaves. Slice the chicken neatly into shards and lay on top. Juice the lime, and in a jar, mix the remaining ingredients, except the sesame seeds. Pour the dressing over the top of the chicken and garnish with the sesame seeds.

LEMON SALSA WITH MONKFISH CEVICHE

You can use other fish for this recipe – scallops would be very good – but it must be sashimi-fresh. Both elements of this dish need to be prepared half an hour in advance. Serve on a hot day.

1 red onion

2 tablespoons parsley

1 tablespoon coriander

2 garlic cloves

1 tablespoon chilli

125 ml olive oil

3 lemons

60 g fresh monkfish

1 lime

Make the salsa first to give it time to mature. Dice the red onion and place in a bowl. Chop in the parsley and coriander. Finely chop the garlic and chilli and add to the mix. Add the olive oil and mix again. Skin and chop the lemons and blend in the flesh. Leave to stand. Slice the monkfish as thinly as you can – it needs to be paper-thin – and lay flat on a plate. Squeeze over the lime juice and leave for twenty minutes. Mix the salsa and ceviche together before serving.

GRILLED RED MULLET WITH PARSLEY SAUCE

This is a lovely summer sauce for any grilled fish. It should take exactly the same amount of time to make as the fish takes to cook. It would also work well with steamed young vegetables or a bean salad.

1 red mullet

1 garlic clove

Sea salt

¼ teaspoon black peppercorns

¼ teaspoon fennel seeds

Handful of parsley

180 ml olive oil

1 large shallot

1 lemon

Turn the grill on high and grill the fish for about five minutes. Pound the garlic, salt, pepper and fennel seeds in a pestle and mortar. Chop the parsley. Add two tablespoons and a little oil to the pepper mix to make a paste, then stir in the rest of the parsley. Dice the shallot and add in with the zest of the lemon and the remaining oil. Squeeze the lemon juice into the mix before serving with the fish.

ROAST CHICKEN WITH ROMESCO SAUCE

If cooking for four or more, then a whole chicken is better than pieces and usually cheaper. If you are just cooking for one or two, thigh and leg pieces work best. This recipe will yield enough sauce to store and use on steamed broccoli or cauliflower, or with a little game meat.

1 onion	Paprika
2 red peppers	70 g chicken
1 fennel bulb	75 g almonds
3 garlic cloves	1 slice of stale bread
6 chillies	4 tablespoons olive oil
2 tomatoes	

First roast your vegetables. Turn the oven up to medium and, in a clean tray, roast the whole onion, peppers, fennel, garlic, chillies and tomatoes. After twenty minutes, add the chicken to roast alongside the vegetables. Cook for twenty more minutes, keeping an eye on the smaller items so that they do not burn. Add the almonds for the last ten minutes.

Remove from the oven and allow to cool. Let the chicken rest wrapped in foil. Put the peppers in an airtight plastic bag so the steam releases the skin. After twenty minutes, peel the peppers and place in a blender. Peel the garlic and add to the blender with the onion, chillies, almonds, tomatoes and a pinch of paprika. Add in the bread, broken into pieces. Pour in the olive oil and pulse a few times. If you need more liquid, add a little water or more oil. The sauce should not be smooth, but will have an interesting texture. Serve with a salad and steamed broccoli.

THAI-STYLE GREEN CURRY

A lot of Thai cooking is, in fact, very alkaline. Coconut milk or cream is alkalising and makes a good base to which many other good things can be added. If you can find fresh young lemongrass or galangal, add these to the mix too. You might also be able to find Thai apple or pea aubergines, which are very authentic and look great.

Coconut oil	250 ml coconut milk
3 garlic cloves	75 g chicken breast
3 slices of ginger root	75 g mango
3 green chillies	1 lime
1 aubergine	Sprig of basil

In a wok or a large pan, warm the coconut oil. Peel and dice the garlic and ginger, chop the chillies, and shallow-fry for a couple of minutes to release the fragrances. Chop the aubergine into small pieces and add to the mix. Stir well. Add the coconut milk and bring to a simmer. Slice the chicken breast into cubes, add to the wok and cook for twenty minutes. Chop the mango into pieces and add for the last five minutes of cooking. Serve with a squeeze of lime juice and basil leaf garnish.

Vegetarian Thai green curry
Curries are great for vegetarian and vegan alkaline eating, not only because of the alkaline coconut milk, herbs and spices, but also as you can add almost any vegetable for a satisfying meal.

If you would like to make this curry vegetarian, leave out the chicken and mango and add some peeled, chopped butternut squash with the aubergine. Toss in some chopped red pepper, mange tout and baby corn five minutes before the end.

MASHED BROAD BEANS AND MINT WITH LAMB CHOPS

Shelling broad beans is a good job for children. If the beans are young, take off the outer skins as well so you just have shiny green kernels.

100 g broad beans, shelled
Vegetable stock
70 g lamb chop
1 garlic clove

1 lemon
1 small chilli
2 tablespoons olive oil
Handful of mint

Simmer the broad beans in vegetable stock for five minutes. Take off the heat and drain. Turn up the grill to high and cook the lamb chop for about three minutes on each side.

Mince the garlic, juice the lemon and finely chop the chilli. Use a fork to mash the broad beans roughly with the olive oil, garlic, lemon juice and chilli. Chop in the mint and mix in well. Serve the chops on top of the broad beans with roast butternut squash, steamed new potatoes or new-season carrots if you like.

5 WAYS WITH COCONUT

Coconut is an almost complete food. In Malay it is called the tree of a thousand uses. The water has isotonic qualities, while the milk is flesh that has been chopped and macerated in water to produce both a cream – the thicker part that rises to the surface when chilled – and the milk itself. It is high in lauric acid, which supports the immune system and is also a good source of manganese. It is high in fat, however, so be careful not to overdo it.

» Coconut milk is a quick meal for a soup or a curry. Add it to pan-fried curry paste in a wok and add some water, vegetables, fish or meat. Good partners include aubergine or monk fish.

» Roll up dried (rather than dessicated) coconut with toasted almonds, apricots, prunes, cinnamon and pistachios for an alkaline snack.

» Coconut flour can be used to make gluten-free cakes. Use one-third less than you would wheat flour, but increase the number of eggs as it soaks up liquid.

» Coconut milk makes an Asian accented rice pudding. Use in just the same way as you would cow's milk and dress with mango slices or passion fruit.

» Make an alkaline chutney by blending freshly grated coconut, coriander, shallots, ginger, garlic, chillies and lemon juice in a food processor to a thick, coarse paste. Add ground coriander seeds, cloves and cinnamon, salt and sugar, and refrigerate until needed.

DESSERTS

Gluts of summer berries and fruits have a whole host of
possible ends – from compotes and glorious salads to stunning
desserts like our showstopper summer pudding.

FRESH FIGS WITH YOGHURT AND HONEY

2 ripe figs   1 teaspoon honey
2 tablespoons yoghurt

Slice the figs in half and arrange on a plate. Serve the yoghurt to the
side, with the honey poured over the top.

BAKED PEACHES WITH HONEY
AND ALMONDS

*This is a good dessert if your peaches are not quite ripe – the cooking will
bring them on.*

1 peach   1 tablespoon crème fraîche
1 teaspoon butter   2 drops vanilla extract
1 teaspoon honey   Flaked almonds, to garnish

Preheat the oven to 180°C. Slice the peach in half, removing the stone.
Place on a baking tray with a topping of butter and a dribble of honey
– it doesn't need too much. Bake for twenty minutes. Meanwhile mix
the crème fraîche and vanilla extract. Toast the almonds in a non-stick
pan and leave to cool. Take the peach out of the oven – it should be
bubbling – and serve with the crème fraîche and almonds.

SUMMER PUDDING

The trick here is to have just enough juice from the fruit to colour the bread without it becoming too soft to hold its shape. As long as the fruit is ripe, you should not need to sweeten it, but you can add a little agave syrup or stevia if you think it will need it. To get a good fruit to bread ratio, it is best to make enough of this to share. The recipe below will serve four, and is a great dinner party dessert served with some natural yoghurt or crème fraiche.

750 g summer fruit – berries, currants, cherries (pitted)

1 loaf of good-quality white bread, slightly stale

Put the fruit in a pan with a tablespoon of water and bring to just under the boil. Add a second tablespoon of water and heat through, without boiling, for four minutes – until the juices flow. Turn off the heat.

Cut the bread into thin slices and remove the crusts. Line a bowl with the bread, cutting it into triangles for the sides and a circle for the base. Pour off the juice from the fruit and wipe the bread slices through it to colour them and affix to the bowl. Put the leftover juice into a pan and simmer gently to reduce. Let cool and store in the fridge. Pour the fruit into the bowl containing the bread and top with another circle of bread. Weight the top down with a plate and a tin. Refrigerate overnight.

To serve, use a thin knife to cut around the bowl edges and turn out onto a plate or serving dish. Cut into quarters, and pour over the sauce.

5
Autumn

AUTUMN

When leaves fall from the trees and we start to crave comfort and calm, it is important to listen to your body. We all have natural, inbuilt rhythms, and the transition from the warmer months to darker days and colder weather is one that can sometimes be difficult. Allow yourself to feel the movement of the seasons, and enjoy this change through your meals and activities – take a walk through woodland or spend time in your kitchen surrounded by chestnuts, game birds and bubbling stews.

SALADS

Salad Nicoise 125

Salad of beetroot, its leaves and anchovy 126

Salad of chicory, pear, walnuts and goat's milk cheese 126

*

SMALL PLATES & SIDES

Swede mashed with black pepper 128

Parsnips with toasted pine nuts 128

Kale with figs and pomegranate molasses 129

Casserole of celery, kale, garlic and caraway 130

Cauliflower with olives 130

*

MAINS

Picada with grilled veal chops 132

Roast rack of lamb, lemon kale, parsnip and carrot mash 133

Stir-fried ginger tofu with broccoli 134

Grilled pineapple with bacon and cabbage 135

Buckwheat pancakes with parsnip and parsley cream 135

Chestnuts with cabbage, gravy and roast quail 136

*

DESSERTS

Warm fruit salad with vanilla and honey 138

Poached pears with cardamom, yoghurt and honey 139

Apple and blackberry crumble 139

Chestnut pancakes with ricotta and pomegranate 141

Castagnaccio 141

START THE DAY

At this time of year, markets are often full of unexpected exotic fruits that make colourful, alkaline salads to start the day. Look also for plums, apples and pears – all great partners for alkaline spices and great for poaching and stewing.

APPLE WARMER

This is a warming tea that can also be made to warm up a cold evening. As you are mulling the fruit, spices and liquid, it is easier to make a big batch of this and then store any leftovers in the fridge – it will keep for up to a week.

500 ml apple juice	1 orange
500 ml water	2.5 cm piece of ginger root
1 cinnamon stick	Pinch of allspice
4 cloves	

Put all the ingredients apart from the orange into a large saucepan and place over a high heat. Take the peel off the orange and add to the pan, then break up the segments and add them too, along with any excess juice. Bring to a simmer, turn the heat down low and leave for twenty minutes for the spices to infuse. Strain and ladle into a cup.

AUTUMN JUICE

1 beetroot and its leaves	1 orange
1 carrot	2.5 cm piece of ginger root
1 parsnip	

Chop all the ingredients into small pieces so that they slip into the juicer easily. Skin the carrot and parsnip if wrinkly. Juice the orange or skin and add whole segments. Trim the skin off the ginger and add to the mix. Juice together. Taste, adding a little water if too strong.

POACHED PLUMS WITH CRÈME FRAÎCHE

Plums ought to be at their best now, but this recipe works for all kinds of fresh fruit (peaches, nectarines, apricots, even cherries) when they are not as ripe as they should be. Make more than one portion (as the recipe below) and keep it in the fridge for a quick and easy breakfast. You could also slake this with vanilla or spike it with a cinnamon stick cooked in the juice.

450 g of fresh plums

1 tablespoon agave syrup

Crème fraîche, to serve

Wash and pick over the plums and remove the stalks. Arrange them over the base of a pan without stacking the plums. Add enough water to come about one-quarter of the way up the plums and bring to a simmer. Add the agave syrup if needed. Cover and simmer until the plums burst, about four or five minutes. Take off the heat and transfer to a bowl. Chill. Serve with a spoon of crème fraîche.

PINEAPPLE AND POMEGRANATE

1 pineapple   1 pomegranate

Both of these fruits will keep, so cut just enough for one serving. Cut straight through the pineapple and carve off the skin. Remove the hard core and chop the flesh. Break open the pomegranate and pick over a segment for the seeds. Combine with the pineapple.

SHARON FRUIT, BANANA AND KIWI

In Japan, sharon fruit is known as the food of the gods, provided it is ripe. It should be soft to the touch.

1 kiwi   1 small banana
1 sharon fruit   1 lime

Use a small knife to cut the furry skin from the kiwi so you have a nice, neat, green cube. Cut into dice or slices as you prefer. Cut the sharon fruit in half and then into thin slices. Dice the banana. Mix the fruit together and squeeze over some lime juice

BLACKBERRY AND WATERMELON

This looks very beautiful. Allow it to chill for half an hour in the fridge before serving.

1 slice of watermelon   100 g blackberries

The trick with watermelon is to slice it thinly so that you can flip the seeds out easily. Then scrape the layer nearest the skin with a spoon to get the juice. Decorate with the blackberries. Chill.

5 WAYS WITH GINGER

Ginger has been recognised in herbal medicine for as many as two thousand years, as a carminative and soother of the intestinal tract. Modern research has confirmed that just 2.5 cm or less of the root can have noticeable effects – as a tea against seasickness, for example, but also for easing aches and inflammations arising from rheumatism.

>> Ginger tea is scientifically shown to help combat nausea, especially in pregnancy. Remove the skin, grate enough to cover the bottom of a glass and fill with hot water. Add lemon or honey if preferred.

>> Ginger is part of the holy trinity in Thai cooking, diced and stir-fried with chilli and garlic. Coconut butter is too strong for many European dishes, but in Thai cooking its high heat resistance lends it to stir-frying the spices and using them to season coconut milk. Add meat and fruit such as pork and mango or beef and papaya.

>> Ginger makes an interesting Asian-style dressing for a salad of lettuce, avocado and red onion. Dice a carrot and a shallot with two tablespoons of grated ginger, a tablespoon of miso, two tablespoons of brown rice vinegar, a tablespoon of sesame seeds, a splash of water and 125 ml grapeseed oil.

>> For an easy side dish to go with grains and spiced meats or fish spike a good quantity of yoghurt with ginger, garlic and cinnamon.

>> Chop rhubarb, grate a chunk of ginger and juice and zest an orange and let it all simmer in a pan with a dash of agave syrup to create a great porridge or yoghurt topping for breakfast.

CARROT AND SQUASH SPREAD WITH CELERY AND SESAME

100 g carrot	Half a celery stalk
100 g squash	Sesame seeds
50 g curd cheese	Paprika

Cook the carrot and squash in vegetable stock or water until soft. Strain and keep back the liquid for stock. Blend the vegetables in a blender adding a little of the cooking water if the mix is dry. In a bowl, use a fork to blend the carrot and squash with the curd cheese. Use a knife to fill the celery stalk with the mix. Decorate with sesame seeds and paprika.

CELERIAC ON TOAST WITH CHIVES, MUSHROOMS AND TRUFFLE OIL

This recipe perfumes the kitchen with the elusive and magical smell of roasting celeriac. If there are any leftovers you can mash it with curd cheese and use as another breakfast spread

1 small celeriac	Chives
2 button mushrooms	Truffle or olive oil
1 slice sourdough bread	

Wash and roast the celeriac whole in the middle of a medium oven for about fifty minutes. Take it out and let it cool a while you prepare everything else. Simmer the mushrooms in broth for five minutes. Remove and slice thinly into crescents for a garnish. Toast the bread. Cut the skin off the celeriac with a large knife so that you are left with a large square. Mash the roasted celeriac with a fork and spread on the toast. Add the mushrooms and finish with a scissor of chives and a drop of truffle or olive oil.

SMOKED TROUT SPREAD WITH DILL

200 g smoked trout fillets

100 g fresh soft sheep's or
   goat's milk cheese

100 g cooked potatoes

1 tablespoon lemon juice

1 tablespoon fresh horseradish

1 tablespoon fresh dill

Pinch of rock salt

Bring the trout, cheese and cooked potato together in a bowl. Using a
fork, lightly mash together so they are well combined. Add the lemon
juice if too dry. Grate in the horseradish. Chop the dill and mix in
with the salt. Leave to infuse for thirty minutes. Serve on warm toast.

BEETROOT, HORSERADISH AND CUMIN SPREAD

200 g cooked beetroot

200 g boiled mealy potatoes

2 tablespoons olive oil

1 tablespoon cream

Pinch of ground cumin

2 tablespoons fresh
   horseradish

Pinch of rock salt

1 tablespoon parsley

Blend the beetroot and potato, using the oil and cream to smooth.
Add the cumin and grate in the horseradish. Season with rock salt and
add freshly chopped parsley.

SOUPS

All the great autumn root vegetables – pumpkin, squash, beetroot, parsnip, swede, carrot – make beautiful earthy soups, either mixed together or on their own.

PUMPKIN AND PARSLEY SOUP WITH PUMPKIN OIL

Pumpkins are wonderfully alkaline and make pretty soups. Butternut is probably the most reliable, but all kinds can make interestingly different soups. You need a good, strong knife to hack through them. Keep the seeds for drying, too – they are alkaline and make a snack in their own right or tossed into salad. Here, the flavour is reinforced with pumpkin seed oil.

750 ml water or	200 g pumpkin
vegetable stock	Bunch of fresh parsley
100 g potatoes	Rock salt
100 g carrots	Pumpkin seed oil

Bring the water or stock to a boil in a large pan. Wash and chop the potatoes into small cubes and add to the water. Skin and chop the carrots and add them. Split the pumpkin in half and scoop out the seeds. Carve off the skin and chop the flesh into small pieces the same size as the potatoes. Add to the pan. Separate the parsley stalks and leaves and drop the stalks into the broth. Cook for fifteen to twenty minutes. Pour into a blender or use an electric wand to purée. Add rock salt to season. Chop the parsley leaves for garnish and serve with a drizzle of pumpkin-seed oil.

LEEK AND POTATO SOUP WITH EGG

The egg is optional in this recipe, but it offers a little extra protein to make a main course for lunch. This classic combination is at its best in autumn, when new potatoes and new leeks are plentiful.

4 leeks	1 egg
1 potato	1 tablespoon crème fraîche
Vegetable stock or milk	Rocket or fresh herbs

Wash and dice the leeks. Peel and trim the potato. Put both in a large pan and pour in just enough vegetable stock or milk (or both) to cover, and simmer for twenty minutes. Remove from the heat and leave to cool a little, then blend to a smooth purée. To serve, poach the egg as you warm up the soup and drop into the middle of the serving bowl. Pour the warm soup over the top, decorate with the crème fraîche and scissor over the rocket or herbs.

CARROT AND NEW POTATO SOUP

The trick here is to grate the carrots – handy if you are in a hurry – and cube the potatoes for contrast. Laces of onion, shards of carrot, squares of potato and nuggets of farro all create a sunset glow.

100 g farro	Bunch of parsley
750 ml vegetable stock or water, plus extra for farro	250 g carrots
1 onion	2 good-sized new potatoes

Cook the farro in the vegetable stock for twenty minutes and set aside. Roughly slice the onion and simmer in vegetable stock in a second pan. Add the parsley stalks. Grate the carrots and cube the potatoes neatly. Add both to the stock. Top up the stock so that the vegetables are just about covered. Cook for twenty-five minutes. Drain the farro and add to the mix. Remove the parsley stalks. Serve with a good smattering of chopped parsley.

POTATO, PORCINI, FARRO AND CHESTNUT STEW

This is a luxurious recuperative broth in which farro and mushrooms star. You can add more or less stock depending on how soupy you would like the finished dish. Fresh mushrooms can be sliced straight into the pan. Cooked chestnuts are sold vacuum-packed. If you have fresh ones, pierce and poach first, then skin before adding.

100 g dried wild mushrooms	4 small new potatoes
100 g farro or pearl barley	1 garlic clove
1 litre vegetable stock or	1 sprig rosemary
water, plus extra if needed	100 g cooked chestnuts
1 shallot	1 tablespoon olive oil

Soak the wild mushrooms in warm water for twenty minutes (if you have fresh, you can skip this step). Wash the farro or pearl barley and cook in vegetable stock or water for twenty minutes, then set aside. Slice the shallot and sweat in a non-stick pan for five minutes. Cut the new potatoes into small cubes and add to the shallot, cook gently so as not to catch and add a little stock if necessary. Crush and dice the garlic and add in. You need to be able to remove the rosemary before serving unless it is very young, so add as a stalk. Cook for ten minutes.

Add the mushrooms – chopped using scissors – and their water. Add more vegetable stock, if needed, to cover Add the cooked chestnuts and farro. Cook on until the potatoes are tender – another ten minutes. Take out the rosemary. Serve with a drizzle of olive oil.

5 WAYS WITH BEETROOT

Beetroot has been used in herbal remedies for centuries, especially for its detoxification qualities, which help the digestive process. The leaves, too, are rich in calcium, iron and vitamins A and B. Beetroot contains the amino acid glutamine, which nourishes the intestinal tract. The redness of the root comes from the betalain antioxidant, which is different from other caratoniod vegetables. Beetroot is, of course, very messy in the kitchen and stains easily. Lemon juice will clean surfaces, including your hands.

>> Beetroot is best wrapped in foil and roasted long and slow. Add halved red onions and leeks for a ragout.

>> Raw beetroot makes a good juice mixed with orange, grapefruit, raspberries and ginger. It can also be grated into a raw salad or shallow-fried with garlic. For a slaw mix, try with fennel, red cabbage, spring onion, soured cream and chia or poppy seeds.

>> Steamed beetroot makes a beautiful salad dressed with nut oil or mixed with orange segments, combined with yoghurt and dill. It pairs well with carrots spiced with caraway and garlic, too. Avoid steaming for too long, as it will lose colour and vitamins.

>> Horseradish (which is also alkaline) might have been invented for beetroot – grate it fresh, directly on top of roasted beetroot. Add a little fresh goat's milk cheese, too.

>> Beetroot's most famous incarnation is, of course, a Russian borscht. Try the alkaline variation on page 152.

SALADS

Add robust nuts, garlicky dressings and autumn fruits to salads to immediately create a substantial meal.

SALAD NICOISE

This is best served tepid. The recipe provides enough for four people, as it is perfect for a weekend lunch, but scale down if making for one.

For the dressing:

2 garlic cloves

175 ml olive oil

2 tablespoons lemon juice

Pinch of sea salt

Black pepper

For the salad:

Vegetable stock or water

8 small new potatoes

Handful of fine green beans

4 free-range eggs

2 Little Gem lettuces

8 small artichoke hearts,
   cooked (bottled)

16 black olives

4 very ripe tomatoes

Half a cucumber

1 tin good-quality tuna
   in olive oil

1 tablespoon chervil

Small handful of basil

Crush the garlic and mix well with the other dressing ingredients.

Put a large pan of vegetable stock or water on to boil. Wash and halve the potatoes and cook for ten minutes. Trim the green beans and add to the potatoes, with the eggs, to cook for another five minutes. Drain and keep the water for stock. Peel the eggs and quarter them.

In a large bowl, arrange the lettuce, potatoes, green beans, artichoke hearts and eggs. Add the olives. Quarter the tomatoes, skin and dice the cucumber and add.

Pour the dressing over the top and mix at the table. Spoon the tuna into the centre. Garnish with chopped chervil and torn up basil.

SALAD OF BEETROOT, ITS LEAVES AND ANCHOVY

100 g red beetroot	1 garlic clove
100 g yellow beetroot	2 anchovies
50 g beetroot leaves	1 tablespoon olive oil
1 egg	1 tablespoon soured cream

Wrap the beetroot in foil and roast slowly, ahead of time, for one hour or longer, depending on size. Remove and leave to cool. Bring a pan of water to the boil and cook the leaves and the egg for four and a half minutes – the egg yolk should still be runny. Drain and line up the leaves in a bowl. Take the shell off the egg. Skin the beetroot under running water, rubbing off the skin with your fingers. Then, using the largest cut on the grater, slice thinly into the bowl.

Make the dressing: crush the garlic and the anchovies with a pestle and mortar and add the olive oil and soured cream. Mix in with the leaves and the beetroot. Add the egg – sliced in half.

SALAD OF CHICORY, PEAR, WALNUTS AND GOAT'S MILK CHEESE

This is an alkaline version of a classic autumn assembly – you want a goat's milk cheese that has a little edge or tanginess. To make it even prettier you could use a mix of red and yellow chicory.

1 head chicory	6 walnuts
1 pear	20 g goat's milk cheese

Trim the base from the chicory and discard any outer leaves that are discoloured or going soft. Dice and toss into a bowl. Using a potato peeler, skin the pear and dice into cubes – keeping the juices, which will form the dressing. Crush the walnuts into small nuggets and add to the bowl. Break up the goat's cheese and scatter over the top of the salad. Toss and leave to stand for five minutes before serving.

SMALL PLATES & SIDES

Mashed root vegetables are one of the ultimate autumn comfort foods, but dark leafy greens are also vital as they provide crucial vitamin C, fibre and calcium as well as beneficial antioxidants.

SWEDE MASHED WITH BLACK PEPPER

This recipe always surprises people. Swede seems unassuming but, here, it is vibrant and dramatic. The pepper is very important.

1 small swede	1 tablespoon cream
1 tablespoon butter	Black pepper

Cut the skin from the swede and chop into cubes. Place in a pan and cover with boiling water. Cook for twenty-five minutes, until soft. Drain off the water. Add the butter and cream. Mash smooth with a fork, keeping it a bit lumpy. Give the mash a good grinding – more than usual – of fresh peppercorns.

PARSNIPS WITH TOASTED PINE NUTS

1 parsnip	1 tablespoon butter
10 g pine nuts	1 tablespoon cream

Peel the skin from the parsnip, top and tail, and chop into equal sizes. Cover with boiling water and cook until soft, about fifteen minutes. Toast the pine nuts in a hot, dry pan, until they start to smell and brown, about three or four minutes. Drain the parsnips. Add the butter and cream, mash and whip up to a light fluff. Scatter over the pine nuts.

KALE WITH FIGS AND
POMEGRANATE MOLASSES

If you can't find pomegranate molasses, use fresh pomegranate and a touch of good-quality balsamic vinegar. You can also use fresh figs for this recipe, so skip the first stage if you are.

5 dried figs	1 tablespoon pomegranate
75 g kale	molasses
4 tablespoons pumpkin	Sea salt
or olive oil	Black pepper
1 lemon	1 tablespoon paprika

Soak the figs in warm water for twenty minutes. Slice the stalks off the kale and then roll up and cut across into ribbons. Simmer for about eight minutes in boiling water. Take the figs out of their water (it can go in the stockpot), squeeze dry and put in a bowl. Use scissors to snip them into smaller pieces, then add the oil, the juice of the lemon and pomegranate molasses and mash well. Drain the kale and dress with the figs, a good grind of pepper and a dusting of paprika.

CASSEROLE OF CELERY, KALE, GARLIC AND CARAWAY

100 g celery	1 tin of tomatoes
Vegetable stock or water	1 tin of borlotti beans
1 garlic clove	100 g kale
Bunch of spring onions	10 black olives
2 tablespoons caraway seeds	1 lemon

Chop the celery and cook in vegetable stock or water for about ten minutes, until soft. Drain. Peel and crush the garlic, dice the spring onions, and drop into a large pan with a splash of water, the caraway seeds and celery. Add the tomatoes and beans. Add a little more stock to make it soupy. Chop the kale, removing the stalks, and add to the mix. Simmer for five minutes, until the kale is cooked. Spoon into serving bowls and serve with the olives, a wedge of lemon a drizzle of oil.

CAULIFLOWER WITH OLIVES

1 medium cauliflower	2 garlic cloves
3 tablespoons parsley	1 tablespoon olive oil
2 eggs	12 black olives, pitted
2 anchovy fillets	

Break up the cauliflower into florets and simmer for about ten minutes, with the stalks from the parsley. The florets need to retain some bite. Add the eggs to boil for the last four to five minutes, depending on size. Drain the cauliflower, discard the parsley stalks, but keep the water for stock. Peel the eggs under cold water. In a small pestle or bowl, make the sauce: mash the anchovy, garlic and eggs and loosen with the olive oil. Place the cauliflower in a bowl and toss well with the dressing. Add the olives and scissor over the parsley. Serve warm, although it is equally good cold. Keep any leftovers for the next day.

MAINS

As it gets colder, you might find yourself automatically piling up your plate or craving the acid foods you used to fall back on. Don't be fooled though – your body needs nutrition from a range of sources, and if you practise mindful eating the portions of protein here will be more than enough.

PICADA WITH GRILLED VEAL CHOPS

Try serving this Spanish sauce with baked sweet potatoes, too.

2 slices of stale bread	1 orange
100 g almonds	Olive oil
6 sage leaves	Sea salt
3 garlic cloves	70 g veal chop
1 chilli	Half a lemon

Set the oven to medium and roast the bread slices and the almonds for about ten minutes, until both are dry but not burnt. Put them in a blender or a pestle and mortar – the blender will make the mix very smooth, while a pestle and mortar results in an interesting texture. Cut the sage leaves small, crush the garlic, snip the chilli, deseed and add all to the mix. Juice the orange – if you are using a blender add it whole, but peeled – and add to the mix with the oil. Pound everything into tiny fragments. Add the salt.

Grill the veal chop for five minutes on each side, depending on thickness. Put a good spoonful of the picada onto the veal, squeeze over the juice of the lemon and serve with spinach, new potatoes and fresh, steamed carrots.

ROAST RACK OF LAMB, LEMON KALE, PARSNIP AND CARROT MASH

Autumn lamb has more flavour than spring lamb. It is a swap between tenderness and flavour. Rack is expensive, but there is little waste. It needs to be cooked as quickly as possible – to get the skin crisp and browned and all fat dissolved, yet with the inside still pink – and then left to stand. This recipe can be easily scaled up or down – allow two small chops per person.

1 onion	1 glass apple juice
3 parsnips	Cream
3 carrots	300 g kale
1 garlic clove	1 tablespoon butter
1 rack of lamb	Half a lemon
Sea salt	

Turn the oven to high. Trim and skin the onion, parsnips, carrots and garlic and chop into equal sizes. Use the offcuts to make a base in the roasting pan, fill with about one centimetre of water and cook in the oven for fifteen minutes – the offcuts need longer than the meat. Rub some salt into the skin of the lamb, add to the offcut vegetables and roast for thirty-five minutes. Remove from the oven and wrap the meat in foil to rest. Add the juices to a small pan with the apple juice and leave to reduce slowly for the gravy.

Steam the vegetables together for fifteen minutes, until soft. Drain, adding a little of their water to the gravy and the rest to a clean pan for the kale. Return the cooked vegetables to the pan and mash with the cream. Trim out the kale stalks with scissors and roughly chop the leaves. Add to the boiling vegetable water and cook for five minutes. Strain the water off into the stockpot and return the kale to the pan with the butter. Squeeze in the juice from the lemon.

Carve the lamb into cutlets, pouring any juice into the gravy, and lay on top of the vegetable mash with the lemon kale to one side and a jug of gravy.

STIR-FRIED GINGER TOFU WITH BROCCOLI

*Greens such as pak choi, peppers and shiitake mushrooms would all work
well too.*

100 g firm tofu

2 tablespoons coconut butter

100 g broccoli

2 garlic cloves

2–3 hot chillies

5 cm ginger root

3–4 spring onions,

Handful of coriander

1 tablespoon sesame oil

1 tablespoon sesame seeds

Drain the tofu and pat dry with kitchen towel. Cut into cubes.

Heat the coconut oil in a wok over a high heat, until it has melted.
Sauté the tofu for two to three minutes, until it is golden and crisp.
Transfer the tofu to a bowl.

Steam the broccoli for three minutes. Dice the garlic and chillies
and add to the wok. Stir-fry for thirty seconds. Peel the ginger and cut
lengthwise into matchstick strips. Add to the wok and cook for thirty
seconds more. Add the broccoli.

Return the tofu to the wok. Slice the spring onions and add to the
wok. Mix everything together and cook for one minute. Turn the heat
off and stir in the coriander. Garnish with sesame oil and seeds.

GRILLED PINEAPPLE WITH BACON AND CABBAGE

This is something of a 1950s cliché, but pineapple and bacon have an unusual affinity. Just be sure the pineapple base is bigger than the bacon loin. If you are cooking for a few people, roast the bacon loin as a whole joint and carve thinly.

1 slice of fresh pineapple	Vegetable stock or water
75 g bacon loin chop	1 tablespoon butter
250 g cabbage	

Turn on the grill, and cover the tray with foil to catch any juices. Carve the pineapple across and trim off the skin so that you have a good steak-style square. Lay the bacon loin on top. Grill for four minutes on each side, flipping the bacon over but not the pineapple.

Chop the cabbage while the vegetable stock or water comes to the boil. Steam the cabbage for five minutes. Drain off the water into the stockpot. Finish with the butter, and serve with mashed potato.

BUCKWHEAT PANCAKES WITH PARSNIP AND PARSLEY CREAM

250 ml milk	100 g parsnips
125 g buckwheat flour	1 tablespoon cream
2 eggs	1 teaspoon honey
Rock salt	1 tablespoon paprika
2 tablespoon parsley	

Combine the milk and buckwheat flour with the eggs, salt, and parsley in a blender. Peel and dice the parsnips and boil for ten minutes, until soft. Thinly cover the base of a non-stick pan with spoonfuls of the batter and fry for one minute, then flip over for another minute and stack the pancakes up ready to use. Drain the parsnips – keeping the water for stock – and mash with the cream and honey and some more parsley. Spread the parsnip mix on the pancakes and fold over. Dust with the paprika.

CHESTNUTS WITH CABBAGE, GRAVY AND ROAST QUAIL

This is a good recipe for when you have family and friends over, because they will not notice that it is alkaline. It involves a very traditional way of making gravy – and the gravy matters here. You can use other game – partridge, pheasant, grouse, pigeon or even chicken. Serve with cabbage, so that you can share the cooking water with the gravy. The cabbage and chestnuts also go very well with vegetarian nut roasts.

1 carrot	100 g cabbage
1 parsnip	100 g chestnuts
1 onion	1 tablespoon butter
1 quail	

Preheat the oven to a medium-high heat and boil a kettle of water. Trim the vegetables into small dice and use to make a bed in a roasting tray. Cover the bottom of the pan with a thumb-depth of water. Lay the quail on top and roast for about twenty minutes, depending on the size of the quail. If you can find them, fresh or tinned vine leaves will stop the bird browning too quickly. Take out the quail, wrap in foil and leave to rest for a good thirty minutes.

Meanwhile, transfer the vegetables from the roasting tray, and the juices, into a smaller pan and simmer to reduce. Shred the cabbage and simmer in a separate pan, along with the chestnuts, for seven to eight minutes. Drain and use the water to top up the gravy. Finish with the butter. Carve the quail and lay on the cabbage and chestnuts. Pour over a little gravy with its vegetables and leave the jug on the table for seconds.

You can use the carcass and some fresh vegetables to make the base of the gravy into a lovely soup with farro and lentils. Put the carcass back on to cook slowly for one hour with water, an onion, and a carrot, then take off the heat and strain. Reheat the stock, add farro and lentils, and simmer until tender.

DESSERTS

In winter, warm desserts are comforting and restorative, and you needn't think that your favourite crumbles and cakes are off limits. Try the chestnut pancakes if you are cooking for a crowd.

WARM FRUIT SALAD WITH VANILLA AND HONEY

You can keep the leftovers from this recipe and eat the next day for breakfast.

100 g papaya
100 g banana
100 g apples
100 g pears

30 g honey or maple syrup
1 vanilla pod
Sprig of fresh mint

Skin the papaya, deseed and cut into squares. Skin the banana and cut lengthwise and then across into squares. Peel the apples and pears and cut into equal-sized squares. Heat the honey or maple syrup in a non-stick pan with four tablespoons of water. Split the vanilla pod lengthways and scrape out the seeds. Add to the honey mixture. Add the fruit and cook for one minute, just to warm through. Chop the mint finely and use to decorate. Serve as is or with crème fraîche.

POACHED PEARS WITH CARDAMOM, YOGHURT AND HONEY

Pears are often overshadowed by apples, but are just as alkaline.

2 pears	1 tablespoon honey
1 tablespoon cardamom pods	2 tablespoons yoghurt

Slice the pears in half and lay in a small pan. Cover with water. Add the cardamom pods and bring to a boil. Lower the heat and simmer for five minutes. The pears need to be pliant, but not mushy. Scoop out the pears leaving the cardamom pods behind. Take a tablespoon or two of the juice and mix in with the honey. Pour the honey mix over the pears and serve with yoghurt.

APPLE AND BLACKBERRY CRUMBLE

This crumble recipe uses no sugar – the fruits should provide all the sweetness. It should be two-thirds fruit to one-third crumble. All kinds of fruit are good for this – from peaches to rhubarb – but this is the original, and the first one of the year.

100 g cooking apples	75 g blackberries
100 g butter, plus	200 g plain or spelt flour
2 tablespoons	

Preheat the oven to 180°C. Peel and chop the apples thinly and lay in the base of a dish with the two tablespoons of butter and the blackberries. For the crumble topping, rub the flour and remaining butter together in a bowl, until the mixture resembles breadcrumbs. Cover the fruit with this mix. Bake for twenty-five minutes, until the fruit starts to burst through to the top and the crust is golden.

CHESTNUT PANCAKES WITH RICOTTA AND POMEGRANATE

For 8 pancakes:

50 g chestnut flour

50 g spelt flour

2 large eggs

Pinch of sea salt

240 ml milk

60 ml water

1 tablespoon melted butter

For the filling:

250 g fresh ricotta cheese

1 teaspoon agave syrup

125 g pomegranate seeds

Fresh berries to decorate

Put all the pancake ingredients into a blender and blend until smooth. Pour into a bowl, cover, and rest for one hour at room temperature. Warm a non-stick frying pan and cook in batches for one minute each side.

Mash the ricotta with the agave syrup and mix in the pomegranate seeds. Spread on to the pancakes and fold into squares. Decorate with fresh berries. Store any leftovers in the fridge.

CASTAGNACCIO

This is a Tuscan dessert. It can be eaten hot or cold, served with ricotta.

300 g chestnut flour

Pinch of sea salt

Water

40 g pine nuts

40 g raisins

2 tablespoons agave syrup

Olive oil

Sprig rosemary

Preheat the oven to 180°C. Sieve the chestnut flour and salt into a large bowl and add water little by little, stirring continuously, until you have a smooth and liquid brown batter. Add half the pine nuts and raisins, and the agave syrup, and stir again.

Grease a large flat baking tray with olive oil and pour in the chestnut batter. Sprinkle with the rest of the pine nuts, the rosemary and raisins and bake for thirty minutes until the cake starts to wrinkle.

6
Winter

WINTER

Winter brings cold nights and shorter days, but also a rich variety of produce to be enjoyed – from hearty roots to fruits such as clementines and persimmons. It is also when we can come together to feast and fête in the comfort of our homes. Use this time to bring people together with a proper alkaline Sunday lunch, or take a dance class to keep your mind enlivened and encourage movement in the digestive system. Winter can be the best time of year in which to focus on yourself, those around you, and the plan ahead.

SALADS

Warm salad of Brussels sprouts, chestnuts and celeriac 155
Warm winter salad of celeriac, farro and pomegranate 155
Seaweed, daikon and cucumber salad 157

*

SMALL PLATES & SIDES

Parsnips with farro and puy lentils 158
Roast celery in a paper bag 158
Old-fashioned mashed potatoes and their skins 159
Potato skins with soured cream and chives 159
Homemade fennel sauerkraut with caraway 161

*

MAINS

Couscous, chermoula and cod 163
Orange, radicchio and French beans with grilled duck breast 164
Pan-fried mackerel fillets with bulgur wheat, pomegranate,
mint, and cucumber 165
Braised chicory with lemon and veal escalope 167
Soft-boiled egg with broccoli and celeriac 167

*

DESSERTS

Orange and pomegranate salad 168
Rich amaranth chocolate cake 168
Baked apple with cinnamon, star anise, vanilla and lemon 169

START THE DAY

Porridge provides other alkaline foods with a route to the breakfast table. It is the perfect partner for a compote of stewed dried fruits or a handful of linseeds and almonds. Oats have a distinct, friendly flavour, which stems from their magnesium, potassium, iron, calcium, vitamin E and vitamin B. They also contain large quantities of soluble fibre. Try the recipes on page 150 when your body needs warmth.

KIWI, COCONUT AND AVOCADO JUICE

Half an avocado   250 ml coconut water
1 kiwi   Handful of spinach
1 lime   1 tablespoon agave syrup

Peel the avocado, kiwi and lime. Add these, and the remaining ingredients, to a blender and blitz. Taste and add a few more drops of agave syrup if you need it.

BREAKFAST BLAST

This makes for a substantial but fast breakfast in a glass when time is short in the morning.

250 ml apple juice   50 g rolled oats
100 g kale   Half a banana, peeled
100 g raspberries or   2 medjool dates
   blueberries   Vegetable tea or water

Place everything in the blender and blitz well. For more liquid, use vegetable tea to dilute. Leave for five minutes to macerate.

SAGE, FENNEL AND MINT TEA

250 ml water

4 sage leaves

Half a teaspoon fennel seeds

Sprig of mint

Slice of lemon

Put the water on to boil. Place the sage, fennel seeds, mint and lemon in a teapot. Just before the water boils, pour it over the herbs. Infuse for fifteen minutes. If you leave this tea to infuse for longer, it will become darker and sweeter from the sage.

POACHED APRICOTS IN GREEN HERB TEA

250 ml water, or enough to cover

100 g apricots

Handful of sage leaves

Bring a kettle of water to the boil. Place the dried apricots and sage leaves in a bowl. Cover with boiling water. Leave to infuse for one hour. Leave in the fridge overnight. Serve with yoghurt.

RHUBARB AND RAISINS

Rhubarb is a blessing through winter – a welcome shot of colour, vitamins and roughage, even if it lacks the flavour of the summer crop.

3 stalks rhubarb

1 tablespoon agave syrup

20 g raisins

Trim any dirty bottoms from the rhubarb – you can keep the flowers at the top – and strip out any woody skin. Chop into short lengths. Cover the base of a pan with water – the juice is very drinkable, so be generous – and the agave syrup (rhubarb can be quite sour). Add in a few raisins for contrast. They will plump up in the juices. Bring to a simmer and watch for the moment the rhubarb bursts, about four or five minutes. Take off the heat. Chill – it should be eaten cold.

POACHED EGG WITH SUMAC AND CHIVES

This grand version of breakfast eggs is brighter and more interesting than most. Two or three eggs a week supports a healthy protein intake. The yolks are alkaline, the whites are acid, so trim the whites with scissors to suit. At the clinic we serve eggs on two very thin slices of ham or turkey ham, but they also go well with a grilled field mushroom. If you cannot find sumac, chilli flakes are also alkaline, or just use a little rock salt. Swap the coriander for chives if you prefer.

1 egg	Butter
1 slice of sourdough or	1 teaspoon sumac
spelt bread	1 teaspoon fresh coriander

Bring a pan of water to the boil. Using a wooden spoon, start to swirl the water clockwise. Drop in the egg and leave to cook for two minutes. Toast your bread and lightly butter. Using a slotted spoon, lift out the egg, drain and trim the white. Lay on the bread. Dust with sumac and scissor over the fresh coriander.

FRESH CURD WITH NUTS AND SEEDS

The meal from flax is more beneficial, nutritionally, than the whole seeds.

15 g of walnuts	80 g curd or quark cheese
15 g almonds	1 teaspoon honey
2 tablespoons flaxseed meal	Half a lemon

In a pestle and mortar, or a small coffee grinder, crush the nuts and seeds together. In a bowl, use a fork to blend in the curd with the nuts, seeds and honey. Squeeze over some lemon juice to make smooth.

PROPER OAT PORRIDGE

Porridge is easy to make, but as you get practised it is noticeably different depending on how much liquid you add and how much stirring is involved. Porridge is best made in two stages – get it started early and come back to it when you are ready to eat. Substitute with nut milks (see right), soya milk or other grains like polenta and buckwheat to ring the changes – the cooking is the same.

75 g porridge oats   200 ml milk

Cover the base of your pan with oats. Turn on the heat and toast for a few seconds before adding the milk. Add the milk in stages – enough to cover to start – and stir. Then add more milk and keep stirring until the mix starts to spit and form little volcanoes. Take off the heat and set aside. When you are ready to eat, bring the pan back to the heat and add a dash more milk and stir as it comes back to the boil. Keep stirring in the milk to keep it smooth.

ALKALINE ALMOND PORRIDGE

Almonds are so healthy, and yet are frequently married with sugar. This recipe offers an antidote, and is full of good things.

40 g almonds   40 g oats
1 tablespoon hempseeds   1 tablespoon chia seeds
1 tablespoon flaxseeds   Berries
100 ml water or vegetable tea   Coconut flakes
40 g quinoa

Blend the almonds, hempseeds and flaxseeds with the water or vegetable tea. Transfer to a small pan with the quinoa, oats and chia seeds. Heat gently, stirring into a porridge-like mix, and adding a little more water or vegetable tea if needed. Serve with fresh berries and coconut flakes.

ALMOND MILK

The general rule for making nut milks is to use double the amount of water to nuts when blending, but you can try out different ratios depending on what you like. You can also add in some pine nuts to this recipe if you like, or try adding vanilla for sweetness and aroma.

150 g almonds
235 ml water

Agave syrup, if needed

Soak the almonds uncovered in water overnight (the longer you soak them the creamier the milk will be). Drain and wash well – they should have plumped up and feel softer. Combine with the water in a blender. Pulse for two to four minutes until milky and opaque. Strain and sweeten with agave syrup if needed.

VITAL VITAMINS

This is a small vegetable spread. You can cheat and lift a similar mix of vegetables out of your minestrone or vegetable tea. Just vary the recipe according to what you have.

200 g carrots
200 g celeriac
150 g potatoes
200 g broccoli

3 teaspoons hemp oil
3 tablespoons fresh herbs –
   chervil, basil, parsley
Pinch of rock salt

Wash and chop all the vegetables. Boil the carrots, celeriac and potatoes in a little water or vegetable stock for three to four minutes, until tender. Then add the broccoli and cook for another ten minutes. Drain the water into the stockpot and put the vegetables in a blender. Blend the vegetables with the oil until fine. Chop the herbs finely, sprinkle over the paste and season with rock salt. Serve with cripsbread or rye toast.

SOUPS

Winter vegetables and soups go hand in hand. There is nothing quite so consoling as a steaming bowl, packed with vegetables, when you have just come in from the rain and wind.

ROASTED BEETROOT SOUP WITH CARAWAY

Soups allow us to sneak in alkaline herbs and spices that are not always easy to find room for in other recipes. This is a classic matching of flavours without any fat at all. By juicing half the beetroot you retain its nutritional vigour, and also get a beautiful colour (a trick that works for carrots, too).

400 g fresh beetroot
750 ml vegetable stock
  or water
2 tablespoons fresh
  horseradish
1 tablespoon caraway seeds
Rock salt
1 orange
1 tablespoon crème fraîche

Clean and wash the beetroot. Wrap two-thirds in foil and bake slowly in the oven for an hour or until a skewer slips in easily. Remove and let cool. Rub the skin off the beetroot under running water. Chop and add to a blender with the vegetable stock. Juice the remaining one-third of beetroot and add to the stock. Add the horseradish and caraway seeds. Blend and season. Warm everything through again gently to serve. Garnish with a squirt of orange juice and the crème fraîche.

SWEET POTATO SOUP WITH GINGER, GARLIC, CHILLI AND COCONUT MILK

The sweet potato is a wonderful alkaline staple. This is a Thai soup that uses coconut milk and stock. Use as much or little chilli as you like. The coconut butter has a high heat threshold, so is useful in Asian cooking.

1 tablespoon coconut butter

1 tablespoon ginger root

2 garlic cloves

Chilli to taste

200 ml coconut milk

300 ml vegetable stock

450 g sweet potato

Rock salt

Coriander

In a wok or wide, deep frying pan melt the coconut butter (you can use the thick cream on top of the tin) and let it warm through. Dice the ginger, garlic and chilli and slow-fry for two or three minutes – don't let them burn. Add the coconut milk and stock. Peel and cube the sweet potato, add to the pan and simmer for about fifteen minutes. Blend until very fine. Drain and season with rock salt. Scatter with chopped coriander.

CREAM OF CELERIAC WITH TRUFFLE

This brings a lovely contrast of earthy celeriac with the magical smells of the truffle. You can use truffle butter or truffle oil, depending on what you can find at this time of year. Fresh truffles would also be wonderful.

750 ml vegetable stock or water	2 tablespoons cream
400 g celeriac	1 teaspoon truffle butter or truffle oil
80 g floury potato	2 tablespoons celerac (or celery) leaves
30 g spring onions	

Bring the stock or water to a boil. Using a large knife carve the skin off the celeriac so that you are left with a square cube. Slice into lengths and then into cubes. Wash the potato and chop to the same size. Cook both in the stock for fifteen minutes. Chop the spring onions finely and add to the mix for the last five minutes of cooking. Take off the heat and blend. Add the cream and blend again. Add the truffle butter or oil and garnish with chopped celeriac leaves.

WINTER GREENS SOUP

Brussels sprouts are plentiful and cheap, but do not overcook them. You could also make this soup using kale or cabbage.

1 onion	1 potato
750 ml vegetable stock or water	3 handfuls of spinach
200 g Brussels sprouts	2 tablespoons double cream

Skin and dice the onion and place in a big pan with the vegetable stock. Trim any dark leaves from the Brussels sprouts and nick off the ends. Add to the pan. Skin and dice the potato, add to the mix and cook for fifteen minutes. Add the spinach and cook for one minute longer, until the spinach wilts. Take off the heat. Blend and add the cream just before serving.

SALADS

Salads are not just for summer. Vegetables such as celeriac work brilliantly in composed concoctions such as these.

WARM SALAD OF BRUSSELS SPROUTS, CHESTNUTS AND CELERIAC

Sometimes vegetables in the right combinations don't really need any dressing. Here they all cook together, too. Use vacuum-packed or frozen ready-peeled chestnuts.

Vegetable stock or water	100 g Brussels sprouts
100 g celeriac	100 g chestnuts

Bring a pan of vegetable stock or water to the boil. Peel the celeriac, cut into batons and add to the water. Trim the Brussels sprouts and add to the water with the peeled chestnuts. Cook for ten minutes. Drain and keep the water for your stockpot. Mix together and serve.

WARM WINTER SALAD OF CELERIAC, FARRO AND POMEGRANATE

100 g farro	Sea salt
Vegetable stock or water	Half a pomegranate
200 g celeriac	1 tablespoon olive oil
1 lemon	Handful of parsley

In a pan, just cover the farro with vegetable stock and simmer for twenty minutes. Cut off the skin of the celeriac and slice into a block, then cut across and into thin sticks. Put them into a second pan with the juice of the lemon and salt. Cover with vegetable stock or water and poach for five minutes. Drain, keeping the cooking juices for stock. Combine the farro, celeriac and pomegranate seeds with a little olive oil and salt. Chop the parsley and stir into the mix. Serve warm.

SEAWEED, DAIKON AND CUCUMBER SALAD

Seaweed has many valuable nutrients and makes a different kind of salad for a change. Dried seaweed is easy to find online if you are not near a Japanese or Korean grocery. You can experiment with this recipe with different kinds of seaweed, all of which provide valuable alkaline nutrients and are available dried throughout winter. Any you don't finish can be kept in the fridge for up to two days.

1 packet dried wakame
1 tablespoon distilled white
    (or brown rice) vinegar
1 tablespoon agave syrup
1 tablespoon black
    peppercorns
3 tablespoons sea salt

Half a cucumber
5-cm piece of daikon
2–3 spring onions
Thumb-sized piece of
    ginger root
1 tablespoon sesame seeds

Soak the wakame in a small bowl of cold water for twenty minutes. Drain and squeeze gently to remove excess water. Slice into lengths. Meanwhile, mix the vinegar, agave syrup, peppercorns and salt with a little water and bring to the boil in a medium saucepan, whisking to dissolve the salt. Leave to cool. Combine with the wakame.

Slice the cucumber thinly, grate the daikon and mix in with the dressing and seaweed. Chop the spring onions small and add them. Cover and chill. Drain off any excess liquid before serving. To serve, grate some fresh ginger on top and toast the sesame seeds before sprinkling over the salad.

SMALL PLATES & SIDES

When the nights are drawing in, roasting and baking become favoured cooking techniques.

PARSNIPS WITH FARRO AND PUY LENTILS

Parsnips were used as a substitute for meat during Lent and work really well in this easy dish. This all cooks in one go, in one pan.

20 g Puy lentils
20 g farro
Vegetable stock
100 g parsnip
1 Little Gem lettuce

2 tablespoons olive or
   pumpkin-seed oil
1 tablespoon lemon juice
Sprig of parsley

Wash over the lentils and farro, add to a pan and cover with stock. Bring to a boil and simmer for ten minutes. Trim the parsnip and dice into small squares. Add to the pan for another ten minutes. Drain. In a serving bowl, arrange the lettuce leaves around the edge and pile the parsnip and farro mix into the centre. Dress with oil, lemon juice and chopped parsley.

ROAST CELERY IN A PAPER BAG

200 g celery
200 g carrots
Thyme
Sea salt

75 g shallots
1 glass of apple juice
Olive oil

Preheat the oven to medium. Cut the celery and carrots into equal-sized pieces and mix them in a bowl with a little water, the thyme and salt. Dice the shallots and add to the mix with the apple juice. Make up a parcel with brown paper and lay everything in the middle. Roll up tightly so the vegetables steam inside. Put on a tray in the oven for thirty minutes. Serve straight away, drizzled with a little olive oil.

OLD-FASHIONED MASHED POTATOES AND THEIR SKINS

Getting mashed potatoes just right is an art. Some recipes use water, but that is not a great idea. You can add milk, though. If you bake your potatoes, scoop out the flesh and mash while still warm. The advantage here is that you get the skins to eat with a herby, soured cream mix (see below).

200 g big floury, old potatoes	Sea salt
2 teaspoons butter	Sprig of parsley
2 tablespoons olive oil	and/or chive stems
2 tablespoons cream	

Set the oven to medium. Wash the potatoes and bake for an hour or so, depending on size. Cut them in half and scoop out the flesh. Use a fork to mash them. Work in the butter, olive oil and cream to get the right consistency. Add the salt at the end and garnish with some chopped parsley or chives.

POTATO SKINS WITH SOURED CREAM AND CHIVES

The skins are not to be overlooked and make a healthy by-product of the mash above. They need to be warm for eating.

1 garlic clove	1 potato skin
1 tablespoon soured cream	1 tablespoon parsley
1 teaspoon chives	

Skin and dice the garlic and add to the soured cream. Dice the chives and add them to the cream, too. Smear the mix into the potato skin. Chop the parsley for garnishing.

HOMEMADE FENNEL SAUERKRAUT
WITH CARAWAY

Sauerkraut ought not to be alkaline. However, it has notable benefits for the fauna in the gut and is essentially a probiotic vegetable. It is very simple to make your own and, as everyone will tell you, it is much better than shop-bought varieties.

1 fennel bulb	1 tablespoon caraway seeds
Sea salt	

Slice the fennel into thin shreds on a grater. Pile up in layers, alternating with a good sprinkling of salt and caraway seeds between each one. Finish with a layer of salt. Mash down each layer as you go using a wooden spoon – you must avoid metal. Cover with a clean, freshly boiled cloth and leave in a dark corner in the kitchen. By the next day, there should be enough liquid to cover the fennel. If not, boil some water, add salt and top up the liquid. In a couple of days, a scum will form, and the fennel will bubble. Skim off the scum each day using a wooden spoon. When the fennel stops bubbling, it is ready to eat – it will take about two weeks.

Korean Kimchi

Another brilliant fermented recipe is kimchi. This Korean side dish can be made with lots of different vegetables, but the classic is napa cabbage. Simply mash salt into sliced cabbage leaves using your hands, adding a similar ratio of salt to the recipe above. Pack into jars, then after twenty-four hours rinse off the salt. Mix in some chopped chilli, garlic and ginger and return to the jar. It will be ready to eat in a week.

5 WAYS WITH CELERY

A single stalk of celery contains just ten calories. Along with its vitamin credentials – C, B1, B6 and K – this garden vegetable is also a prime source of potassium.

>> Along with carrot and apple, celery forms the basis of almost every green juice. Blend with kale, spinach, avocado and a fruit juice such as apple or pineapple for a vitamin shot.

>> Braised celery with apple makes a great vegan centrepiece for a meal. Cook both, covered, with a glass of water or half and half apple juice for twenty minutes.

>> Use young celery leaves in the middle of a watercress salad and dress with cider vinegar, honey and olive oil. A few soaked raisins or currants could also feature. For a crunchy alternative, use the celery stalks with green and red apple chunks and walnuts dressed with lemon, mustard and oil. To make it even bigger, shred in some red cabbage and fennel, and top with curd.

>> Pep up a boring green salad by combining celery, fennel, cucumber, spring onions, watercress and lettuce dressed with oil and lemon and a scattering of dill.

>> Celery features in many a soup and makes a good version on its own. Just sweat down with onions and vegetable stock and finish with a dash of cream. Blend well until smooth, and garnish with walnuts.

MAINS

Try including winter fruits such as pomegranates and blood oranges into your lunches for a burst of alkaline vitamins. Pears and citrus fruits are good too, and work well in salads.

COUSCOUS, CHERMOULA AND COD

Big white fish are at their best in winter, when the waters are cold. A little couscous is enough here and will be balanced by the alkaline vegetables, herbs and spices. The couscous and chermoula would also go well with roasted or grilled aubergines.

2 teaspoons cumin seeds

1 lemon

Bunch of coriander

1 teaspoon cayenne pepper

2 teaspoons sweet paprika

4 garlic cloves

2 tablespoons vegetable stock

½ tablespoon coarse sea salt

70 g cod steak

50 g couscous

Olive oil

Toast and crush the cumin seeds. Skin the lemon. Place in a blender with all the other ingredients, except the cod, couscous and oil. Blitz quickly – you don't want a smooth mush, but something bumpy with texture. Smear the cod steak on both sides with the chermoula. Cover and marinate for one hour. Pour a kettle of hot water over the couscous so that it is just covered, and leave to fluff up while the fish cooks. Place the cod in a medium oven and bake for ten to twelve minutes, depending on thickness. Serve with steamed broccoli and a drizzle of olive oil.

ORANGE, RADICCHIO AND FRENCH BEANS WITH GRILLED DUCK BREAST

Good-quality big oranges, like navels, are best. Blood oranges bring a splash of soured colour in the middle of winter, so use these if you can find them.

70 g of duck breast   Half an orange
100 g French beans   1 head radicchio

Put the grill on high. Cook the duck breast for ten to twelve minutes, as pink as you like. Trim the French beans and boil for five minutes. Drain and set aside. Peel the orange and slice into rounds. Take the duck breast off the heat and leave to rest for five minutes. Arrange the radicchio leaves on a plate. Mix the French beans and orange together and place at the side. Carve the duck thinly and lay on top.

PAN-FRIED MACKEREL FILLETS WITH BULGUR WHEAT, POMEGRANATE, MINT AND CUCUMBER

The point of this dish is to be very generous with the herbs. If you are avoiding meat, you needn't include the mackerel. Try mixing in a little sheep's milk feta cheese instead, or some freshly steamed broad beans.

150 g bulgur wheat	Quarter of a pomegranate
1 teaspoon tomato purée	Half a cucumber
2 garlic cloves	1 lemon
2 spring onions	1 tablespoon olive oil
2 tablespoons parsley	Rock salt
2 tablespoons mint	3 tablespoons yoghurt
1 tablespoon chilli	80 g mackerel fillet
2 tablespoons walnuts	

Pour boiling water over the bulgur wheat – enough to cover. Stir in the tomato purée and leave to stand for twenty minutes. Chop the garlic, reserving a little for later. Chop the spring onions, parsley, mint and chilli. Crush the walnuts and pick out the seeds from the pomegranate. Stir everything into the bulgur wheat. Chop the cucumber and add half to the mix with the juice of the lemon, olive oil and rock salt. Mix the rest of the cucumber with the yoghurt and the reserved chopped garlic.

Pan-fry the mackerel fillets in a non-stick pan for two minutes on either side. It is an oily fish and should not need any fat in the pan. To serve, lay up the bulgur wheat salad, place the fish on top and the yoghurt to the side.

5 WAYS WITH PUMPKINS

Pumpkins are members of the carotenoid family and are rich in vitamin A. Low in calories, they are a good source of fibre. The seeds are also high in the amino acid tryptophan, which supports the body's ability to develop the mood-enhancing hormone serotonin. Pumpkins contain more potassium than bananas.

» Steamed pumpkin mash is a great winter favourite. Carve the flesh from the pumpkin and steam for fifteen minutes until soft. Mash and serve with butter and pepper.

» Pumpkin can be simmered in vegetable stock with onions, carrots, celery, rosemary and bay for forty minutes for a steaming hot ragout. Garnish with parsley and soured cream.

» The Italians have various recipes for pumpkin with pasta. Try roasting the pumpkin with sage and shallots and serving with fat wholewheat rigatoni and fresh goat's milk cheese.

» Pumpkin and pineapple make surprisingly good companions in a curry, with quick-fried garlic, ginger and chilli and garnished with coriander. Simmer the pumpkin in coconut milk for twenty minutes before adding pineapple chunks to warm through.

» Half cover pumpkin, garlic, chilli, onion and chard with stock in a deep frying pan with a lid and braise for twenty minutes. Serve on its own or with some steamed greens.

BRAISED CHICORY WITH LEMON AND VEAL ESCALOPE

Chicory transforms magically when cooked. This recipe uses butter, but you could just as easily use water, wine or cider. The bitterness of the chicory offsets the veal beautifully, but could just as easily be served with mashed root vegetables and steamed greens.

1 head chicory	Half a lemon
10 g butter	Sprig of parsley
70 g veal escalope	

Take a pan that is wide enough to fit the chicory. Split the chicory lengthwise in half and lay in the pan with the butter and just enough water to half cover. Cover and simmer for twenty minutes. Take off the lid and cook the juices down a bit more, so there are just a couple of tablespoons left as sauce. Grill the escalope for two minutes on each side. Serve with a few drops of lemon squeezed over the meat and the chicory on top. Chop the parsley for garnish.

SOFT-BOILED EGG WITH BROCCOLI AND CELERIAC

Everything here can be cooked quickly in one pan. This is a simple and quick main dish to eat for dinner.

100 g celeriac	1 egg
100 g broccoli	1 tablespoon pumpkin-seed
Vegetable stock or water	or herb oil

Chop the celeriac and the stalks of the broccoli into equal-sized batons. Bring a pan of vegetable stock or water to the boil. Poach the batons for five to seven minutes, until soft. Add the broccoli florets halfway through the cooking. Add the egg and cook for five minutes. Drain the liquid into your stockpot. Peel the egg and quarter over the vegetables. Drizzle with pumpkin-seed or herb oil.

DESSERTS

Trying to avoid sugar and wheat can seem like a daunting task, but when you break the refind sugar habit only a little of an indulgent dessert – like our chocolate cake – will be enough.

ORANGE AND POMEGRANATE SALAD

In Japan, dessert is often fruit – a simple, yet fresh way to cleanse the palate after a meal.

1 orange
2 tablespoons
    pomegranate seeds

1 tablespoon mint leaves
Black pepper

Peel the orange and separate the segments. Arrange on a plate. Sprinkle the pomegranate seeds over the top and garnish with the mint leaves. Grind over some black pepper before serving.

RICH AMARANTH CHOCOLATE CAKE

This cake will also work with spelt, wheat or quinoa.

200 g dark chocolate
200 g butter, softened
1 tablespoon agave syrup
6 large eggs

1 teaspoon vanilla extract
1 teaspoon sea salt
250 g amaranth flour

Preheat the oven to 180°C. Roughly chop the chocolate and melt with the butter in a bowl. In another large bowl, combine the agave syrup and eggs. Beat until the mixture is fluffy and has doubled in volume. Beat in the vanilla and salt. Stir in the chocolate mixture. Sift in the amaranth flour and stir to combine well. Pour the batter into a prepared cake tin. Bake for forty to forty-five minutes, until the cake is set and jiggles only slightly when the tin is gently shaken. Allow to cool completely before slicing.

BAKED APPLE WITH CINNAMON, STAR ANISE, VANILLA AND LEMON

This is a real winter classic, and is simple but very rewarding.

1 cooking apple
25 g raisins and sultanas
1 lemon
1 cinnamon stick

1 star anise
1 vanilla pod
1 tablespoon crème fraîche
Flaked almonds

Core the apple and stuff with the raisins and sultanas. Make a parcel for the apple with foil. Peel the zest off the lemon and pack into the parcel with the spices and two tablespoons of water. Seal tightly. Bake for twenty minutes at 180°C. Serve with crème fraîche and flaked almonds.

ACKNOWLEDGEMENTS

I would like to say thank you to Heinzi for the good collaboration and the joy when tasting the receipes; Drew for his unbelievable help, patience, good spirits and wisdom; to Silvia and the team at Elwin Street for the opportunity; to all my patients who have helped me learn; and, last but not least, to my wife and my children for all of their support and love.

Modern Books would like to thank everyone at the FX Mayr Health Center for their help in creating this book, Drew Smith for his contribution, and Uyen Luu, Sally Hamer and Drew Smith for their beautiful photography.

Resources

To purchase base powder and other alkaline health products, please visit The Organic Pharmacy at www.theorganicpharmacy.com.

If you are interested in testing your body's pH levels, you can purchase litmus strips from Micro Essential Inc. USA. Please visit www.microessentiallab.com.

For more information about *The Alkaline Cure*, please visit www.thealkalinecure.com.

For more delicious alkaline recipes and inspiration, please visit www.alkalinecanteen.com.

For more information about the FX Mayr Health Center, please visit www.original-mayr.com.

Photo Credits

FX Mayr Health Center: p. 8. Getty Images: pp. 26, 27 (Maren Caruso), 38 (Simon Wheeler Ltd), 129 (Nicholas Prior), 136 (Philippe Desnerck). Sally Hamer: pp. 2, 6, 45, 59, 63, 67, 71, 79, 142, 143. iStock: pp. 43 (Scrambled), 112, 120 (oksix). Uyen Luu: pp. 31, 73, 77, 86, 89, 95, 99, 102, 105, 108, 115, 119, 122, 127, 131, 140, 149, 153, 156, 160, 164. Shutterstock: pp. 14 (Oliver Hoffman), 16 (Brian A Jackson), 19 (Balazs Kovacs Images), 32 (zcw), 37 (Dionisvera), 47 (MaraZe), 49 (Studio Barcelona), 54, 61 (Mauro Pezzotta), 55 (Rodica Ciorba), 55 (sabyna75), 57 (ksena2you), 68 (Chanasorn Charuthas), 74 (voranat), 82 (Juthamat89), 83, 97 (Vasily Menshov), 83 (Viktar Malyshchyts), 85 (Gita Kulinitch Studio), 90 (Sailorr), 92 (Shane White), 100 (Snowbelle), 106 (Garsya), 112 (Buppha Wuttifery), 117 (Jiang Hongyan), 113, 124 (images72), 129 (Sergio33), 134 (NinaM), 113, 138 (inerika), 144 (topnatthapon), 145 (Adisa), 145 (TrotzOlga), 159 (Sakarai), 162 (Africa Studio), 168 (bergamont), 171 (Magdanatka). Drew Smith: pp. 4, 5, 24, 170, 175. Alessandra Spairani: pp. 10, 11, 15, 35, 41, 52, 53, 80, 81, 110, 111. Joe Woodhouse: 57.

INDEX

This edition published in Great Britain in 2017 by Modern Books
An imprint of Elwin Street Productions Limited
14 Clerkenwell Green
London EC1R 0DP
www.modern-books.com

ISBN 978-1-906761-61-5

10 9 8 7 6 5 4 3 2

Printed in China

Disclaimer: The advice and recipes in this book are intended as a personal guide to healthy living. However, this information is not intended to provide medical advice and it should not replace the guidance of a qualified physician or other healthcare professional. Decisions about your health should be made by you and your healthcare provider based on the specific circumstances of your health, risk factors, family history and other considerations. See your healthcare provider before making major dietary changes or embarking on an exercise programme, especially if you have existing health problems, medical conditions or chronic diseases. The author and publishers have made every effort to ensure that the information in this book is safe and accurate, but they cannot accept liability for any resulting injury or loss or damage to either property or person, whether direct or consequential and howsoever arising.